LORD MAYOR TRELOAR HOSPITAL AND COLLEGE

By

G.S.E. Moynihan

Best Wishes

G. Moynihan

Published by PAUL CAVE PUBLICATIONS LTD.
74 Bedford Place, Southampton
Printed by Brown & Son (Ringwood) Ltd.

Published September, 1988

©

G.S.E.M.
and
P.C.
ISBN 0-86146-072-3

Acknowledgements

I extend my grateful thanks to those members of the staff of the Hospital and the College who have been kind enough to provide articles to help with the contents of this book. It is invidious to pick out a few from among so many but I must thank, in particular, Mr. J. A. Wilkinson, Mr. P. Bayliss and Mrs. J. Mayhew for their unstinted help and encouragement.

I should like to make the point that space has prevented me from including a history or of mentioning all departments of the Hospital. This has, of course, no bearing on their worth or contribution to the Hospital; it is naturally understood that the Hospital runs as a team and each person is an important cog in this machine.

I am also indebted to Professor P. Webb who provided the original impetus for this book.

Finally throughout this account "Lord Mayor Treloar Orthopaedic Hospital" is referred to as the "Hospital" (unless further clarification is needed) and Sir William Purdie Treloar, Bart. as "Treloar".

G.S.E. Moynihan.

This book is to commemorate
the 40th anniversary of the
National Health Service
and
the 80th birthday of Lord Mayor
Treloar Hospital and College.

The founder – Sir William Purdie Treloar, Bart.

LORD MAYOR TRELOAR
CRIPPLES' HOSPITAL AND COLLEGE
ALTON

CONTENTS

PART I

1908 — 1920

In The Beginning

When you've shouted "Rule Britannia," when you've
    sung "God save the Queen,"
When you've finished killing Kruger with your mouth,
    will you kindly drop a shilling in my little tambourine
For a gentleman in khaki ordered South?
He's an absent-minded beggar, and his weaknesses are great -
He is out on active service, wiping something off a slate -
And he's left a lot of little things behind him!

Kipling.

The land on which Lord Mayor Treloar Orthopaedic Hospital was built
was part of the Chawton Park Estate and was sold to Sir Alfred Harmsworth
(later Lord Northcliffe) by Mr. Montague Knight.

The Hospital was originally built by public subscription with the help
of the "Daily Mail" in 1901 for sick and wounded soldiers returning from
the Boer War and was then named, The Princess Louise Hospital, but always
known locally as "The Absent Minded Beggars' Hospital" (after the poem
by Kipling).

However, the Boer War ended in 1902 — before the Hospital was
commissioned.

On completion the Hospital was officially handed over to the Government
at a luncheon held in the Hospital in July, 1903. This was presided over
by Sir Alfred Harmsworth and attended by both the Princess Louise, Duchess
of Argyle and the Duke of Argyle. The Hospital was then run as an R.A.M.C.
Unit under the command of the G.O.C. Aldershot.

Its life as an Army hospital was brief for the R.A.M.C. evacuated the
Hospital in approximately 1905 when the buildings were left in the hands
of a caretaker until taken over by Sir William Purdie Treloar in 1907 in
a dilapidated state.

Arms of Sir William Purdie Treloar, Bart.

Blazon:
   Or on a Mount Vert an Oak Tree Proper fructed Gold on a chief nebuly Gules three Lures of the first.

Crest:
   Two Arms embossed vested Azure cupped or the hands grasping a fasces fessways head towards the dexter proper pendant therefrom by a Chain or an Escutcheon Sable charged with a Bezant.

1. The Arms are a pun on the name TRELOAR, comprising a TREE and (THREE) LURES (used for Hawking)
2. The Crest: The Fasces, or Lictors Rod, was carried before the Roman Consuls by the victors, as an ensign of the Superior magistrates: it is often now given to those who have held magisterial office.
3. The helmet is open and facing the front, Sir William being a Knight and Baronet.
4. The Shield has on it the Hand of Ulster the badge of a Baronet.
5. The Shield is encircled by the Lord Mayor's Chain of Office, his Mace and Sword also being shown.
6. The Motto means "Ancestry is established by honour" — it is also the motto of the Stewart family.

John Walker (Rouge Croix) 13.1.48

Sir William Purdie Treloar, Bart., J.P.

Treloar was born on 13th. January, 1843 (the son of a Cornishman from Helston) in rather humble circumstances over a warehouse where his father carried on his business of coconut fibre mat making in Holland Street, Southwark. The main headquarters of the firm was moved to a much better situation at the bottom of Ludgate Hill in 1868 and it appears that the firm must have been prospering for the family, at the same time, moved to a substantial house in Blackheath.

Treloar's education was largely at King's College School in the Strand but he left school at the age of 15 and worked in the firm from the bottom upwards until he became a partner. On 20th March, 1865 he married a Miss Annie Blake and it appears to have been Mrs. Treloar who first succeeded in getting her husband interested in the care and condition of the many poor and crippled children who then wandered the streets of London. In December, 1881 he was elected a member of the Common Council of the City of London and, presumably, just before this must have become a member of the Lorimers' Guild (since only members of the City Guilds could be elected).

Having no children of their own Treloar and his wife adopted two — their nephew, Royston, and a girl, Florence, who, after his wife's death, became his constant companion and to whom he referred to as "Little Wench".

Treloar's interest in the poor children of London progressively increased and in 1892 he and his wife, with the support of the City Council, and in collaboration with the 'Ragged Schools Union', took over what came to be known as 'The Hamper Fund'. This had been started by the *Daily Telegraph* whose appeals brought in a considerable volume of money. The hampers of food and drink were distributed to disabled children in London on New Year's Day. In the first year these amounted to 200 but over the years increased to some 7,100.

Treloar kept 'open house' for local children and was known as "Uncle" to them all.

In his capacity as a Justice of the Peace, when sitting on the Bench, he often had brought before him in the mornings several small children, cold, wet-through and miserable, on the charge of "wandering the streets". But these children had nowhere else to go!

Thus was sown the seed of an idea in Treloar's mind for the provision of an institution to care for these unfortunate children.

The Common Cryer and Serjeant-at-Arms informed Treloar in 1892 that he had become Alderman of the Ward of Farringdon Without and he became known as the "Children's Alderman".

Seven years later he became a Sheriff of London and, in the same year, the second Boer War broke out. The City made a splendid effort to collect sufficient money to equip and enrol the 'City of London Imperial Volunteers' (about 1,800 men) who were despatched to Cape Town. As a result of the time and enthusiasm he devoted to this project, Treloar was knighted by Queen Victoria at Windsor.

Funding of the Hospital and College

Anticipating his appointment as Lord Mayor of London the following year, Treloar, in 1905, declared his intention of raising a fund during his Mayoral year to found an institution for London's disabled children. The objects of this institution were twofold:

(a) the treatment of children of both sexes up to the age of 12 who were suffering from tuberculous disease of the bones or joints;

(b) the training of crippled boys from 14-18 years of age in skilled handicrafts to enable them to earn their own living.

Lord Mayor of London in November, 1906, Treloar immediately launched 'The Lord Mayor's Little Cripple Fund' with the object of raising £60,000. Donations were sent by King Edward VII and Queen Alexandra; street hawkers of Ludgate Hill had a penny collection; the *Daily Telegraph* launched an appeal; members of the Stock Exchange collected money, pugilists and friends held a benefit performance at a boxing hall; the City Corporation gave £1,000 and there were concerts, stage performances, balls and dances.

Queen Alexandra herself opened a most successful three day fête at the Mansion House which raised the magnificent sum of £12,000. From this was born the Queen Alexandra League (whereby money was collected by children from all over the country). Thus, Queen Alexandra's Rose Day came into being which was, in fact, England's first flag day.

Within his Mayoral year, Treloar exceeded his target by £10,000 and it was now time to look for a site for his institution.

Lord Mayor Treloar
CRIPPLES' HOME

THE Treasurer, Sir William Treloar, Bart., has much pleasure in stating that Messrs. SCHWEPPES Limited, the Purveyors of Mineral Waters to His Majesty the King and H.R.H. the Prince of Wales, have placed at his disposal whatever Lemonade, Ginger Ale, Ginger Beer and Proset, and "Vin de vie" (the Non - Alcoholic Wine) he can sell at this Fête, so that the proceeds may go to the Funds of the Home

Treloar was an enthusiastic fundraiser — and once convinced of the need for a "Little Cripples Hospital", the Royal family, the City and the business community responded magnificently.

Above is a notice inserted in the programme of the Queen's Fete held at the Royal Hospital, Chelsea in June, 1909 in aid of the Queen Alexandra League of Children to help the new Hospital at Alton for poor crippled children.

A Hospital and College are Born

Through Mr. J. Hall Richardson, of the *Daily Telegraph*, Treloar learned that there was an unoccupied hospital, comprising some 70 acres, at Alton for which the War Office had no further use. He came to Alton on Friday, 22nd March, 1907 to inspect the property, approved of it and set about the formidable task of getting the land transferred, with the help of Mr. (later Lord) Haldane, Secretary of State for War. This involved an Act of Parliament which was rushed through at the end of the Parliamentary session with the proviso that should the Hospital ever cease to exist the grounds and buildings must revert to the Crown. Thus the embryo of the 'Lord Mayor Treloar Cripples Home and College' came into being. Shortly afterwards the Hospital was re-named 'Lord Mayor Treloar Cripples Hospital and College'.

There was a lot to do. A water supply had to be installed, which included two huge water towers (still in existence — items 41 & 42 on map) and the upgrading of a special siding named, 'Alton Park' Railway Station — part of the London and South Western Railway, Alton to Basingstoke line — primarily for the delivery of coal but also for the use of passengers. Coal was still delivered to this siding as recently as 1959. Fire precautions had to be devised, drains and boilers installed and electricity connected to the scattered buildings.

Ten acres of gardens were laid out as an orchard and kitchen garden to supply fruit and vegetables and provision was made for pigs and poultry. A large aviary was built on top of the hill on the western boundary to house indigenous birds to "awaken the minds of the children".

The ward buildings consisted of two main blocks of ten wards each and each ward contained ten beds. These wards were grouped around a semi-circular corridor (commonly called 'The Chico') which afforded a ready means of access. The buildings had windows on three sides and a glass enclosure on each end to give the maximum amount of sunshine thought necessary for tuberculous disease. The floors were covered with linoleum, the walls painted white and the ceilings cream.

The Hospital was ready for occupation and the first 18 patients were received at Alton Station by Treloar and his wife on 8th September, 1908.

Sir William and Lady Treloar receiving the first little patients at the Railway-Station, Alton, September 8, 1908.

Drawing by G. L. Stampa from photographs.

The First Resident Medical Officer

With little to offer — a salary of no more than £200 per annum and a new appointment at that, it was not surprising that there were no suitable applicants for the post Resident Medical Officer. So, once more, Treloar took the matter into his own hands. Treloar was an ex officio Governor of St. Bartholomew's Hospital and on one of his formal visits to this hospital he was talking to Mr. C. B. Lockwood, a Consultant Surgeon, in 'The Square' and asked him if he could recommend a suitable young man for six to 12 months to oversee the commissioning of the Hospital at Alton — perhaps someone studying for a post-graduate qualification as "he would have plenty of time to study". At this precise point, and quite by chance, Dr. Henry Gauvain walked across 'The Square' and the situation was explained to him. But his interests were elsewhere since he had already applied for a University Lectureship in Gynaecology at McGill University in Canada which would provide him with ample opportunity for research. Understandably 29 year old Gauvain, who had just qualified, refused Treloar's offer.

Nevertheless Treloar turned on his charm and asked Gauvain to talk over the needs of the new Hospital and its future and, under Treloar's influence, Gauvain withdrew his original refusal and said that he was willing to be considered for the post, the details of which were thrashed out at de Keyser's Restaurant in London! The day after accepting the post as Medical Superintendent, Gauvin received confirmation that he had, in fact, got the job in Canada. To his eternal credit he did not inform Treloar of this.

Following an inspection visit to the Hospital, Gauvain wrote to Sir Ernest Flower (Trustee and Alderman of the City of London and Secretary of the Alton Project) submitting a forthright report. Gauvain considered that the first object of the Hospital should be to obtain a high level of cures or, at least, improvements for without these "the institution would be dragged (down) to the level of a petty Convalescent Home and become more a subject of derision and ridicule than anything else." He insisted that the Resident Medical Officer should have complete autonomy, accept all responsibility and be dedicated to his work. He was convinced that he could undertake this work and was competent to do so and that he could do a lot for the Hospital and vice versa. In the event he was accepted on his own terms (although the terms rankled).

So Gauvain started his career at Alton (where he acquired the nickname of 'The Earl') in August, 1908 and eventually became an international figure.

Sir Henry Gauvain

The original hospital, 1908.

The First Matron

The post of Matron to the Hospital was advertised at a salary of £80 per annum, plus board and lodging. Miss Janet ('Robby') Robertson was the successful applicant currently working as Home Sister in the Hospital for Sick Children at Great Ormond Street. It is said that the chief reason Treloar chose her was because her surname was the same as his mother's maiden name! Be that as it may, Miss Robertson was an ideal choice. She was a small, stocky and very determined woman who tempered discipline with kindness. She hated smoking but would put up with Gauvain's (some say 'offensive') South American cigarettes and his pipe smoking without a murmur. Nevertheless when obliged to work in a smoky atmosphere she registered her objection by hanging all her clothes outside on her balcony to air. Nursing staff were forbidden to smoke, of course.

Arriving at the new hospital at Alton.

Settling in.

Development — 1908-1920

Gauvain, initially, encountered problem after problem, particularly with his dealings with the Medical Board. For example, after his appointment he visited the Chairman of the Board, Mr. J. H. Morgan, Senior Surgeon at the Charing Cross and Great Ormond Street Hospitals, to be greeted with:

"I see you come from St. Bartholomew's Hospital and I cannot imagine, if you have any ambition at all, why you should accept the job which is now offered you. I will tell you frankly; it might be a suitable place for a young man going in for some higher examination, who wanted ample time to read, or for a sportsman who was keen on hunting, fishing and shooting, but as for starting a career in a place like this, it is ridiculous."

At the first meeting of the Board, held in Morgan's house in Harley Street, Gauvain arrived early and, whilst waiting in the consulting room, one of the members of the Board, Sir Thomas Allbutt, came over to him and said:

"There's one thing that we must do; we must all stick together in keeping this young man, Gauvain, down. He must realise that his work is not to cure the patient, but just to run a home for cripples."

Not a good beginning! But relations did improve later on.

On one noteable occasion Gauvain asked if he could have *sterile* dressings for the open sinuses and the terse reply from an emminent visiting London Surgeon was "Use some of Treloar's old carpets!"

Gauvain was not allowed many of the things which he requested. He wanted to install a Pathology Department and an X-Ray set for instance, but these requests were refused as it was considered "completely unnecessary for the treatment of tuberculous bones and joints and if the children wanted medical attention they should be sent to London to see a doctor!" The X-ray set was, in the event, donated by a private patient of Gauvain's and operated by Mrs. Gauvain.

In July, 1908 Treloar visited Jacques Calvé at the Hôpital Maritime, Berck-sur-Mer, near Bologne. Calvé specialised in the treatment of tuberculosis of children with particular reference to conservative treatment and heliotherapy (sunray treatment). On Treloar's recommendation Gauvain also visited Calvé (who later became a great friend) and on return evolved a system whereby:

children suffering from tuberculosis were treated out of doors and exposed to the rays of the sunshine; and

abscesses were aspirated (drained) as opposed to being incised (lanced).

The aspiration of abscesses was an innovation. Gauvain's maxim was "to open a cold abscess was to open a door to death." Previously children

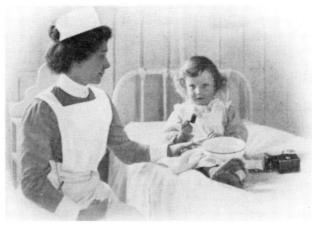

THE FIRST FEW WEEKS – The hospital
opened in August, 1908 and settled down so
quickly that in May, 1909 the pictures on
this page were published in a brochure on Sir
William Treloar's exciting project.
The pet dog below was called "Lord Mayor."

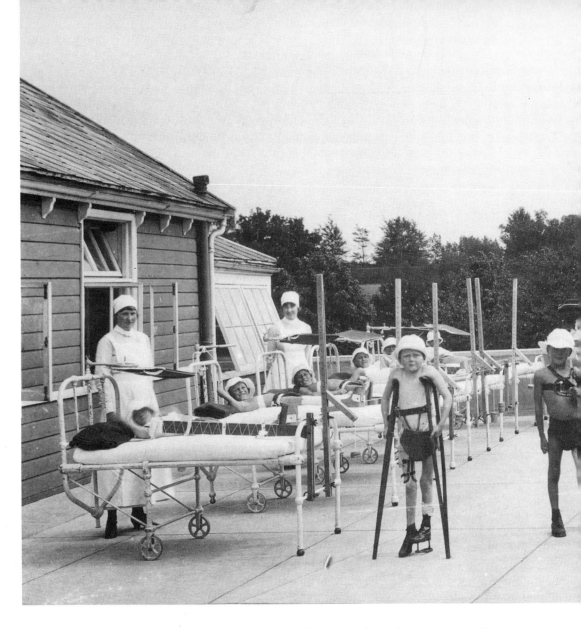

suffering from open sinuses or scepticaemia were, in this country, all too
often, treated in basement wards (to isolate the infection from the rest of
the hospital) which were dark, cold and almost airless. Once this new approach
to treatment had proved successful it subsequently received international
approval but Gauvain pioneered the way in the United Kingdom.

Gauvain was born in the Channel Islands and, therefore, was used
to the bright light and sunshine, so it is not surprising that the use of
heliotherapy was such a feature of the treatment of the children in the
Hospital.

The Hospital was run on strictly conservative (in both senses) and

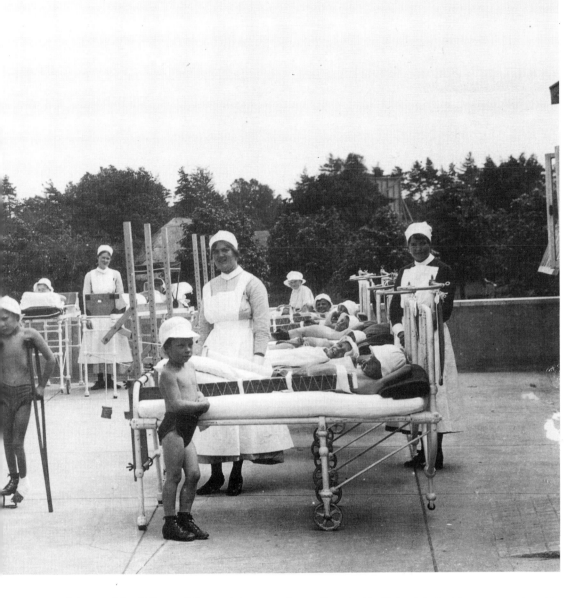

hierarchical lines. The reins were kept firmly in Gauvain's hands.

Applications for admission for children under twelve years of age suffering from skeletal tuberculous disease were received from a variety of sources — from the surgeon attending the case, from the Matron of the Hospital in which the patient was nursed, from officials of other charitable organisations or from the child's parents. These applications were scrutinised by the Medical Superintendent himself and if in doubt the children were referred to the Hospital's Dispensary in London prior to admission. Children suffering from phthisis (pulmonary tuberculosis) were not eligible as they would have been a source of danger to other patients.

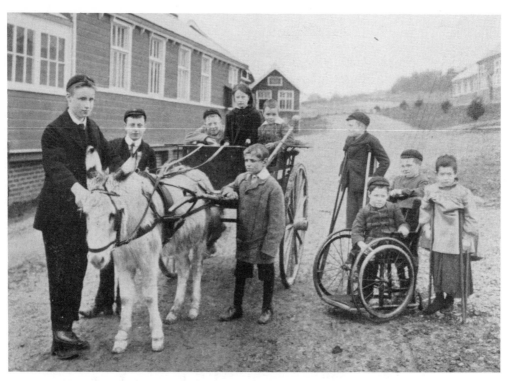

Starting off on a visit to the woods.

During the early part of the twentieth century social conditions, particularly in large cities, were appalling. Disabled children begged in the streets and many were literally starving. Thus on arrival the little patient was often pale, ill-nourished and very pathetic. The child was isolated in one of the Observation Wards for the first fortnight or three weeks to prevent the spreading of any latent infectious disease (including the common cold) and to acclimatise the child to open-air treatment.

As far as possible cases of the same nature were placed together in the wards and every child strong enough was taken out of doors all day long. Gauvain maintained that a healthy child was a happy child and, conversely, a child made happy was helped to become healthy. Therefore, it helped treatment to make the patients happy and contented, and every endeavour was made to this end. Indeed success in its efforts earned for the Institution the title of the 'Happy Hospital'.

Upon admission to the Hospital all clothing in which the child had arrived was set aside until discharged and whilst the patient was under treatment was entirely clothed at the Hospital's expense. This was undertaken by the Alton Cripples Clothing Guild whose President was the Lady Burnham and the Secretary was Miss Florence Treloar (Treloar's adopted daughter).

Waving to the horse-drawn bus.

College boys off to dinner – winter, 1908-9.

In brief, apart from an ample, but plain diet, treatment consisted of:

Rest;
Child fitted with appropriate apparatus;
Immobilisation of affected joint in plaster of paris;
After removal of plaster, leather support fitted with steel supports;
Celluloid splint fitted;
Heliotherapy, supplemented by sun lamps, all the time;
Abscesses aspirated.

All equipment mentioned above was made individually, as required, in the Hospital; the College provided the leather supports.

The Hospital differed from all other institutions in that, whilst the majority of Cripples' Homes were merely asylums where physically disabled children were cared for, the function of this Hospital was: "Firstly the treatment of the deformity and improvement of health and secondarily to give education of a wide nature to awaken interest in their surroundings so that, on discharge from Hospital or College, the children would be physically, and in most cases intellectually, the equal of children of their own class who had not been similarly handicapped."

Visiting to see patients, in the early days, was confined to one afternoon a week for one hour. Later this was extended to a Sunday, but Sunday travelling was not then approved of. No visiting at all was allowed between New Year's Day and 31st March — to some extent this was justified since many of the children were somewhat frail and without antibiotics any chest infection, or the like, would be serious. Many of the parents, in any case, could not afford the fare from London to Alton and back. There was a small discretionary fund but this could only be used if the child were very ill indeed.

Recognition came from the British Medical Association in 1910 when members visited the Hospital to view the work done and to attend a lecture demonstration by Gauvain. The Hospital was now 'on the map'. Indeed it was now a national Hospital admitting children from nearly every county in England and Wales. It should be remembered that children suffering from tuberculous disease of the bones or joints were, at this time, debarred from admission to General Hospitals owing to the long duration of treatment which was necessary to ensure success. The average length of stay in the Hospital was from one to three years. Results, however, were good. Over 90% of the patients admitted to the Hospital were discharged cured — a figure not approached by any similar establishment in the world. What a wonderful record!

However, it has to be said that those children terminally ill were sent

Rest – and hope!

to the C. of E. Sisters of Wantage at the Church of the Holy Rood, Worthing. At one time they ran St. Mary's Home in Turk St., Alton. Were these figures included, then, of course, the success rate would have been lower.

At about this time the first celluloid splints were developed to Gauvain's specification and subsequently made by the teenagers in the College. Later, Gauvain's wife devised a method by which these celluloid splints were made non-flammable. This was the first time such splints had been used in the United Kingdom and represented a great breakthrough.

The First Royal Visit

Queen Alexandra took an immense interest in Sir William Treloar's imaginative project. Here she is enjoying being saluted by three of the young patients.

Queen Alexandra paid a private visit to Alton on 26th July, 1912, accompanied by Queen Amélie of Portugal (both ladies were dressed in black). They came by train and were met by Treloar and his co-Trustees, and a 'considerable throng' in the meadow opposite the siding.

Queen Alexandra conversed with every child as it was the wish of Her Majesty "that no little one should feel that he or she had been forgotten or not taken notice of." When one child requested a flower, the Queen dismantled her bouquet so that each child, in a ward of 20, should have a flower apiece.

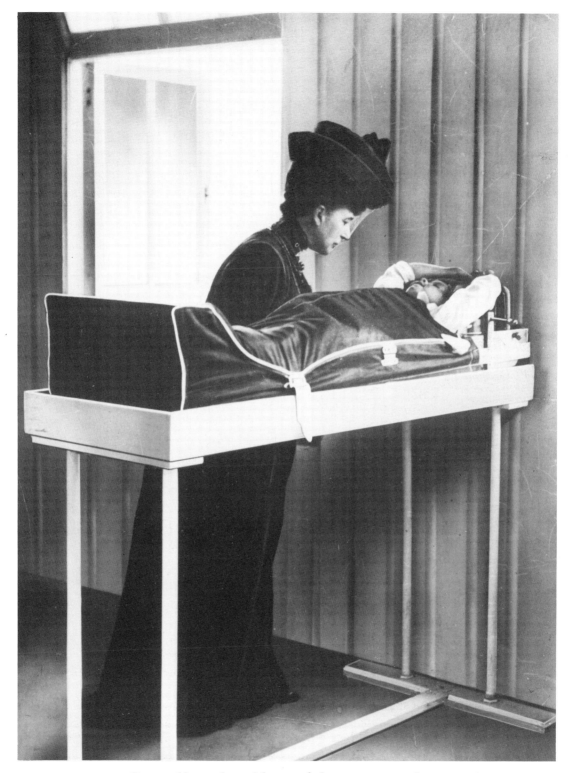

Queen Alexandra with one of the youngest patients.

Alexandra House

With an ever increasing waiting list children were, in 1914, waiting a long time for admission. There were vacant wards, but no accommodation for extra nurses. A further appeal was, therefore, made for funds to build new quarters for the nurses and the First Festival Dinner was held at the Merchant Taylor's Hall, London on 13th May, 1914, presided over by the Rt. Hon. Arthur Balfour, MP. The response was generous, as always, and on 18th February, 1914 the foundation stone of Queen Alexandra's Nurses' Home was laid by the Earl of Northbrook (19 on map) and was completed in three months! This was officially opened by Queen Amélia of Portugal on 17th June, 1914.

Such was Treloar's enthusiasm and optimism that construction work actually started before he had raised the money to pay for it.

Departure – some of the earliest of the young patients leaving the hospital after a course of treatment.

Alexandra House – the Nurses' Home – was opened in June, 1914.

THE HAPPY HOSPITAL . . .

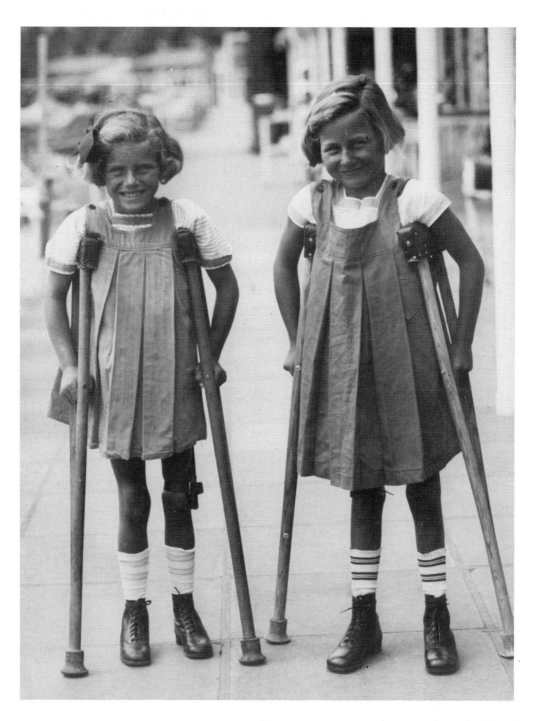

Now what is that photographer up to?

One delightful story has to be told. Treloar, when staying in the Trustees House (26 on map) at the Hospital, would visit the wards every day and speak to each child individually. At that time there was a child from Wales whose father was visiting him. The father asked the child if Sir William Treloar came in to see him often. "Oh, yes, Daddy," said the child, "he comes to see me every day but he doesn't sleep in the ward."

And they were brave – Henry Gauvain plastering a young patient.

35

The Hospital and World War I

The war had a twofold effect upon the Hospital and its work. It was now difficult to arrange public metings and there were few entertainments which meant a considerable loss in income. At the same time there was a marked increase in the number of applications for admission and included in these were many whose fathers were fighting for the Empire.

The Hospital was extended with marquees in order to accommodate the war casualties. College students tilled ten acres of garden and provided fresh fruit and vegetables; they also reared pigs and poultry so, to some extent, the Hospital was self-sufficient (40 on map).

A special ward, then called 'The Fourth destroyer Flotilla Memorial Ward' was established "to the glorious memory of the officers and men of the Flotilla who lost their lives in the Battle of Jutland." In the plans for the rebuilding of the Hospital, after the First World War, provision was made for the Naval Wards in which appropriate memorials would be placed recording names of those who fell. The purpose of the wards was to provide free treatment for the children of men of the Royal Navy and Mercantile Marine and especially for orphans of those who had given their lives for the Empire. The first two orphans were accepted in 1915, one from Portsmouth and one from Chatham, both of whose fathers were lost in the sinking of *HMS Invincible*.

Work continued, as far as possible, but under great difficulties. Electrically heated mattresses were now installed in one ward which solved the problem of keeping the patients warm in the open air.

The Out-Patient Department of the Hospital in London afforded a means of keeping in touch with ex-patients and assisting many who had been discharged. One such patient, treated for spinal caries, was now a soldier! Further After-Care Clinics were established in Wales and Portsmouth, each visited by medical staff twice a year.

It is interesting to note a few of the annual salaries paid in 1914:

Gauvain	£600
Mr. Salt (College Master)	£250
Matron Robertson	£110
Chaplain	£100
Dr. Pattison (Asst. Medical Officer)	£150 + £78
Head Teacher	£165
Typist (London office)	£104
Queen Alexandra League	
Mr. Weekes, Secretary	£400
Mr. Harper Assistant Secretary	£250
Miss Massey Bookkeeper/Typist	£105

Miss Robertson with the 1920's domestic staff.

Above: Matron Janet Robertson with a group of the early teachers of the Hospital school.

Below: The 'Castle' in the background was built by some of the earliest boys at Alton Park. The castle still survives near the hospital's car park.

The Hospital School
by Luath Grant Ferguson
(the Head Teacher)

Follow the main path through the wood at the far corner of the Hospital grounds, after a hundred yards or so, turn off to the left, through the thick growth of saplings (you will now be knee-deep in ivy and leaf-mould, but press on) you will soon reach the heart of the Queen Alexandra Wood (How many hospitals have *Royal* woods of their own?) and just a few yards up the hill you will stumble on a small rectangular bed of concrete. Already shattered by rain, frost and wind-felled trees, half hidden by layers of moss and lichen, this is all that remains of the Forest School built in 1908 on the lines of the Forest School at Charlottenberg, near Berlin (or the summer classroom of Treloar's Hospital School).

A strange idea, it must seem to the planners of today, to push, pull

Below: Off to nature study.

Among the daisies.

and generally herd disabled children across rough pasture up a steep gradient, through rough woodland, over a quarter of a mile from the main Hospital. It tells us a lot about the attitudes of those first planners. If Treloar and his illustrious team were determined to reach their goal, why shouldn't crippled children?

There are photographs of the children blinking into the sun filtered by the canopy of leaves above them. They seem happy and alert, flattered that a photographer should have pursued their trail quite so far.

What, in 1988, is the pharmacy, eighty years earlier was the winter schoolroom. Here that early photographer attempted to portray the children at work, in wheelchairs, baskets and frames. Several faces are blurred because his subjects simply would not sit still! The lady teacher, in her long, dark skirt and blouse with its leg-o'-mutton sleeves, stands calm and confident as well she might. Beneath her feet she has high quality coconut matting — one of the popular lines produced by Treloar's own firm in Ludgate Hill, London. The other equipment is sparse and uninspiring — a blackboard (boasting a most unlikely addition sum), a bare table, a map of Great Britain showing all the counties, and another of the World by hemispheres. Even

The Forest School, 1909.

A view of the aviary in 1909.

1908-9 winter classroom for children at the hospital.

in black and white the extent of the Empire is clear. During the time the children were under treatment such education as their condition permitted was given to these patients above the age of five years.

David Lloyd George (then President of the Board of Education) visited the School in 1911 and was so impressed with it that he supported legislation to introduce similar hospital schools throughout the country.

That first informal experiment in special education lasted until 1913 when the School was certified by, and under the direct supervision of, the Board of Education and the educational work was based on the lines in the Board of Education's code for the teaching of 'physically defective' children. The Headmistress, Miss Amy Lee, had considerable experience in this field; she was aided by five assistant teachers. Children received $5\frac{1}{2}$ hours instruction each day and the teachers actually worked in the wards from 8.45am to 11.45am and, again, from 1.30pm to 4.30pm. As the children were generally recumbent, apparatus and lessons were arranged to meet individual cases. Reading, writing, arithmetic and nature study were taught in the mornings and the afternoons were devoted to handwork, singing and recitation. It was considered that handwork was particularly suited to develop mental powers as well as manipulative skills. Subjects included were drawing, designing, basket work, rug making, pottery design and 'chasing'. In addition girls were taught plain and fancy needlework. The children knitted vests and bedsocks for their own use. Each child had to write a letter home every week in school time. Religious instruction, as in the Hospital and College, was in accordance with the faith of the parents.

In 1919, the Marine Hospital at Sandy Point, Hayling Island opened but there was to be no escape from School and two teachers were appointed to run a small school for the Hayling Island pupils. Gauvain was a regular visitor and often enjoyed a romp in shallow water with the younger patients.

The School had its own Girl Guide Company and Boy Scout Troop (in addition, to the Scout Troop run by the College).

The College students were doing well at their various trades but there was concern over their need for continuing education. Miss Amy Lee was brought in and given still more teachers; for over twenty years all school teaching of the College students was carried out under Miss Lee's supervision. The School now had ten teachers, all but one unmarried ladies (excluding those attached to Hayling Island and the College).

Originally the school had only taught children from the age of five, but the Annual Report of 1922 indicates that "the Hospital continues its work as a special school certified by the Board of Education and approved by the Ministry of Health and was the first institution of its kind to be approved as a Nursery School for children up the age of five years."

By 1923, Miss Lee had married Mr. Richard Aitkin (Steward or Bursar at the hospital).

She continued as Headmistress for another ten years. By the time she retired in 1933 the School was well-established and was highly thought of throughout the world of special education — students and other visitors arriving from training colleges all over the country, as well as from other hospital schools run on the same lines as those at Treloars.

For twenty four years the School and College were served by an all-female teaching staff. No men, other than those instructing the boys in trades, were appointed until 1932.

At the outbreak of World War II in 1939 the Hayling Island unit closed down for the duration and the children returned, with their teachers, to Alton. Teaching at Treloars carried on throughout the second World War years without interruption. In spite of dog-fights by fighters overhead and a high level of military traffic throughout the neighbourhood, the routines established by Miss Lee and Gauvain carried on with better and better results. Academic standards were rising. The School was clearly bringing students within reach of higher education. Integration — of a sort — of children with physical handicaps into mainstream schools was commencing and in the year of the great Education Act itself!

When the Hospital was taken over by the National Health Service, the Hospital school became the responsibility of the Hampshire County Council and took its place as one of the County's Special Schools.

In 1951, the Hospital diversified and adult wards were introduced. By 1970 there were only four wards which had survived from the original Hospital. Ten years later further wards were closed when the Hospital was on the brink of closure. This was a difficult time for everybody at Treloars. With the future in doubt for so long, many valuable staff were forced to move on. The School did not escape and by 1982, the teaching staff had shrunk to two. With Hayling Island long since sold, the College thriving as one of the leading Independent Special Schools in its field and Treloar's old summer and winter schools long forgotten, it might well have been the end of the School's honorable history as numbers on the Children's Wards had been dropping steadily.

Since then, however, numbers have risen again and much has happened. With its new rôle as a Community Hospital, clearly defined within the district, Treloars has much to offer — not least its School. A new nursery section opened in 1984, occupying the former crêche facilities (once the original College dormitories). The unit, called 'Bushy Leaze' (after a wood to the west of the Hospital) caters mostly for pre-school children with special needs from an area about twenty miles across. The nursery team works closely with Health professionals and after only four years is already much respected in the nursery world.

The Hospital School's numbers are now rising again and the partnership with 'Bushy Leaze' is proving invaluable. On the wards, there have been many exciting developments. For the very young children, a trained play-specialist has been working with theatre staff, developing play programmes to prepare the children for the business of having an operation. Computers and other technical aids are now familiar furniture on the wards. The school children now come into greater contact with adults on nearby wards, especially with the elderly residents of the 'Mary Rose' Unit. Since 1984, East Hampshire District Council has paid for holiday play-schemes each summer.

From the 1960s onwards, the greatest and most satifsying change has been the encouragement of parents to help in the care of their own children on the ward. The three-way team-work between the nurses, teachers and parents is something the School values highly.

The Marine Hospital

Following on from Gauvain's heliotherapy treatment it was considered that an ideal arrangement would be to have an establishment at the seaside. The requirements were sunlight, fresh air, salt water and sandy soil. Gauvain had, in fact, pinpointed a suitable site on Hayling Island but owing to lack of money and the war nothing came of it. However, six years later Treloar saw an advertisement in *Country Life* for a freehold house (Sandy Point) on the coast with 60 acres of land. When he discovered that this was the identical property to which Gauvain had drawn his attention, he immediately bought it saying, "The hand of Providence is again pointing." The house was adapted and a pavilion to accommodate 100 beds was planned.

On 19th April, 1919 Treloar laid the foundation stone on which was inscribed the motto of the City of London (what else?) 'Domine dirige nos' ('Oh God Direct Us'). With his typical sense of humour Treloar would recount the tale of a subsequent visit by Sir Alfred Yarrow, who, not being

Lord Mayor Treloar Cripples Hospital, Seaside Branch, Hayling Island.

Paddling on the sands at Hayling Island.

a Latin scholar, asked the foreman what the inscription meant. 'We are not TT here'! came the swift reply. Shortly after the opening of the Hospital a French ship the *Monte Grand* was wrecked off the coast and the shipwrecked sailors were all accommodated in the cottage at Sandy Point.

Sea treatment by dipping into the water.

47

There was a sad side too — during a game of football on the beach, the ball, inevitably, was kicked into the sea. A little boy called Henry Innes tried to retrieve it but in so doing was swept away by the strong current. Another boy, Arthur Campbell, gallantly went into the sea on his crutches grabbed Henry's shirt and pulled him to the shore, there willing hands dragged Henry to safety — not so Arthur, by now, he had lost his crutches and unable to stand on his one leg was rapidly swept away by the strong current and drowned.

At Miss Florence Treloar's suggestion the Trustees erected a tablet to Arthur Campbell's memory which can be seen today in the chapel.

Apart from this unfortunate incident it was a happy place. Both patients and staff loved Sandy Point and it continued its good work until the outbreak of the Second World War when it was immediately requisitioned by the

Hayling Island was great fun. After sea-bathing patients sat around a brazier with their feet in hot water, drinking hot cocoa.

48

Happiness on the beach.

Admiralty and the patients and staff were hurriedly evacuated to Alton. It re-opened in May, 1946.

Mr. Alexander McLean (of McLean's toothpaste) generously gave £100,000 to rebuild Sandy Point. He had requested that a large white palace should be erected which could be seen by every boat which entered Spithead. But with the intervention of the war the re-building was never undertaken and all the money was absorbed by the N.H.S.

Some of the 1908 nursing staff. (Below): Miss Janet Robertson with her 1920's nursing team.

Orthopaedic Nurse Training

by J. Knight

Records show that nurse training at the Hospital had already begun by 1909. On 30th November of that year Matron reported to the Trustees that "three probationers had satisfactorily completed three months' trial and were eligible for appointment at Treloars."

Most orthopaedic hospitals, including Treloars, ran a programme of training within their own hospital and awarded their own certificate. In 1936, a national orthopaedic training syllabus was drawn up and approved. The Hospital deserves a special place regarding the training of orthopaedic nurses, since it was E. Stanley Evans (later to become Medical Superintendent) who was one of a number of people concerned with standards and quality of orthopaedic care. He chaired the sub-committee whose remit was to draw up the National Orthopaedic Syllabus. The first state orthopaedic nursing examinations were held in 1937 and 15 orthopaedic hospitals, including Treloars, entered candidates. Since 1937 nearly 900 nurses have been successful in obtaining the Orthopaedic Nursing Certificate and Diploma.

In 1942, the Joint Examination Board was formed which oversaw orthopaedic training nationally and E. Stanley Evans became its first Chairman. This body governed the training until responsibility was handed in March, 1988 to the National Boards.

The majority of nurses started training at 17 years, the course lasting for one year. Alexandra House — the Nurses' Home — was opened in 1914. The Trustees "had endeavoured to plan it with everything for the comfort and well being of the nurses" as it was recognised that they played a very important part in the care of crippled children. Gauvain writes, "The proposal to lay down a hard (tennis) court has been received with great satisfaction from the nursing staff." Dancing classes were arranged during the Winter months under the "guidance of a professional teacher of dancing." "By such wholesome recreation the amenities of life at the Hospital are greatly increased, a nurse's health is benefited and the efficiency of her work not only does not suffer but is improved."

Miss Janet Robertson, the Matron, was a charming, but strong, character and in spite of her somewhat Victorian attitudes was loved by all the nursing staff. She was, indeed, a strict disciplinarian brought up in, what might be described as, the Florence Nightingale attitude to nursing. She visited all the wards of the Hospital every day unless some urgent matter prevented it when the visits were undertaken by her Deputy, Miss Brown, a formidable, strong-minded woman who was both Deputy Matron and Warden of the Nurses' Home. Both sisters and nurses stood in considerable awe of her.

Miss Robertson was strict upon nursing staff's appearance and as she was so frequently to be seen around the Hospital it was not uncommon for nurses to be reproved for some error of dress or for hair wandering outside their starched caps. In Miss Robertson's day there was never any shortage of applications for nursing posts and the nurses were of a high calibre and well-educated.

Lunch was at 12.45pm in the nurses' dining room. All nurses met daily at Matron's office and lined up in order of seniority, then, with Matron leading, they progressed in procession to the dining room. Junior nurses were responsible for opening the door for their seniors.

Dances were held for the nurses to which the medical staff and a few carefully selected guests were invited. The medical staff (then all male) were expected to dance first with the Ward Sisters and secondly with the nurses but they must never dance more than once with any one nurse. One newly arrived Houseman actually danced three times with the same probationer and was summoned to Matron's office the following morning and duly reproved! Doctors were allowed to take out Sisters for a meal or to the cinema or to the theatre. Nurses had to 'sign-out' and state where they were going and with whom. Matron allowed no local boy friends into the Hospital.

During the winter months the Manager of the only cinema in Alton was requested to start the afternoon session half an hour earlier so that the young nurses were able to return before dark.

It was clearly stipulated that sisters who went riding should put on a long coat in order to cover up their trousers or breeches.

Sister Phyll Bryant, who came to the Hospital in 1946 to train as an orthopaedic nurse and retired recently, gives an insight into the life led by the nurses in the late 1940s. Although nurses had comfortable surroundings their life was hard compared with the life of a student nurse today. The nurses' day began at 6.30am when they were called by the maids. Nurses had to be on duty at 7.30am and no nurse was allowed to miss breakfast. Night Sister sat in the dining room and a roll was called. After the ward round each nurse was acquainted with her duties for the day, mealbreaks and off-duty times.

Nurses kept their own rooms tidy and made their own beds. If rooms were left untidy books etc. would be piled in the middle of the bed by the Home Sister and a badly made bed would have the bedclothes pulled off. A note was left in the offender's room to report to Home Sister. Most nurses had a room to themselves. No nurse was allowed to visit the room of a senior nurse (but, of course, they did). Friday evenings were 'sewing evenings' and nurses collected their linen baskets with clean linen and sat

In Sir William Treloar's lifetime members of the Royal Family and outstanding politicians came to the Hospital on Founder's Day each year. On this occasion Mr. Neville Chamberlain (later to become Prime Minister) was among the guests. He is seen above on the left hand side of Matron Janet Robertson.

in a circle in the recreation room. Here nurses made up their clean caps (which had to be gathered evenly at the back) and did any mending as necessary. Home Sister was in attendance and she usually read an article of interest from the *Nursing Mirror*. No one was allowed to talk. All nurses had to be in their rooms by 10pm each night, and Home Sister did a room check. Any nurse found to be absent had to report to Matron's office the next day. Nurses had one day off a week. But nurses had fun too with free passes to the local cinema and invitations to the officers' mess at Sandhurst — but in the latter case the nurses were handpicked by Matron.

Discipline was no laxer in the 1950s. Young David and Michael Cane (sons of the Hospital Secretary) used to take the nurses out for a drink locally but the nurses had to be back before closing time and, naturally, they were often late. However, the girls' friends had kindly left a window open at the back for them to get in. The nurses were duly 'posted' back by the young men through the open window and all was well until one of them entered her room only to find the Home Sister standing there waiting for her!

When student nurses first arrived they went into the Preliminary Training School (PTS) before going to the wards. Nursing practice and theory were taught in the school, including how to lay up dressing trolleys for specific procedures. All the required instruments and equipment had to be learnt by heart. Bedmaking was meticulously taught; nurses had to know how to make the different types of bed and all nurses were tested before going onto the ward.

In 1951 the hospital began to take adult patients and it was considered that "admission of adult patients was another progressive step from a training point of view." Nurses undergoing orthopaedic training were prepared for the first part of their general registration. Treloar Hospital was affiliated to Westminster, King's College, Royal Hants., County Hospital at Winchester and the Prince of Wales Hospital; nurses after completing their orthopaedic training undertook the remainder of their general training in one of these hospitals.

Nurses undergoing orthopaedic training did well on the whole. A report from 1950 states of the May set "all candidates passed and one gained Honours". In November, 1950 "88% of students passed and two nurses were awarded Honours."

By 1951 recruitment of nurses was causing concern. The report of that year reads "recruitment constitutes a major difficulty ... it is hoped that the agreement with the General Nursing Council will not entirely preclude the engagement of student nurses under the age of 18 years. The Hospital is eminently suitable for girls between the ages of 17 and 18 years to begin their training as nurses in the childrens' wards" (Nurses' training in orthopaedics could begin one year earlier than for general training).

Since 1951 the need for children's beds steadily decreased so most of the wards were adapted for adult use. The different focus of orthopaedic care obviously affected the training of orthopaedic nurses. Children were no longer admitted with diseases like tuberculous bones and joints needing the "unremitting attention" of skilled nurses over many months, even years. Adults undergoing joint replacements and conditions such as osteoarthritis and rheumatoid arthritis dominated. Trauma patients were much in evidence and so long as we have the mototcar it will continue to be so. Many of these patients would need orthopaedic surgery in later years as a result of their original injuries.

Orthopaedic surgery is the fastest growing branch of surgery and changes in society, in health education and in technology have created different needs and a changing emphasis. Advances in technology have produced exciting new materials which enable the patient to become independent quickly using less hospital and nursing time.

Certain changes took place in general nursing towards the end of the 1970s when responsibility for educational standards in nursing became the

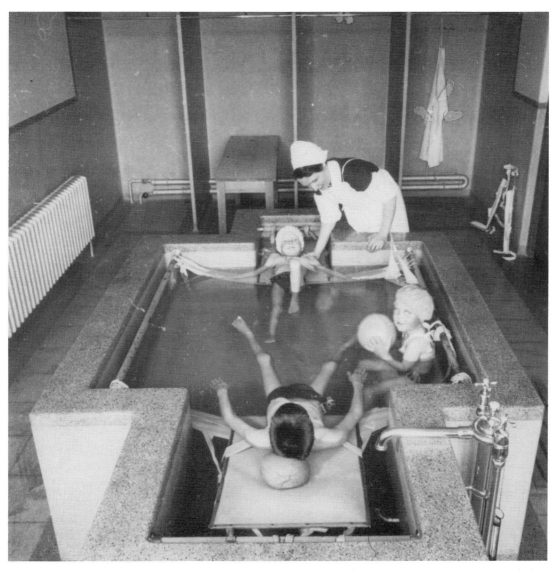

The Hydro-Therapy Department – early days.

direct responsibility of the National Boards. At the beginning of the 1980s the Joint Examination Board and members of the National Boards formed a committee with a view to drawing up a new syllabus for orthopaedic nurse training. Hospitals already running orthopaedic course training were invited to develop and submit a curriculum to the National Boards for approval. The Hospital won approval in January,1987 for a maximum period of five years. All orthopaedic nurse training in England now comes under the auspices of the English National Board.

Nurses' Prizegiving (c. 1920) – on Founder's Day. Lady Mayoress, Sir William Treloar, the Lord Mayor of London (Mr. Sheriff Eves) and Sir George Makins (President, Royal College of Surgeons).

Nurses in training are in a very different position to-day. Nurses work a 37½ hour week and have the freedom of choosing whether or not to live in the Nurses' Home. Nurses are more in partnership with the ward sisters and share in patient care. This focus of caring is called the 'nursing process' which centres care around four basic steps to ensure nurses give each patient individual care. This process of caring may be a new concept to nurses undergoing general training but it is not new to orthopaedic nurses as shown by an extract from Gauvain's first Report—"anything approaching routine treatment is avoided, each patient's case is carefully studied and its individual requirements met".

Founder's Day: Lord Mayor and party on terraces.

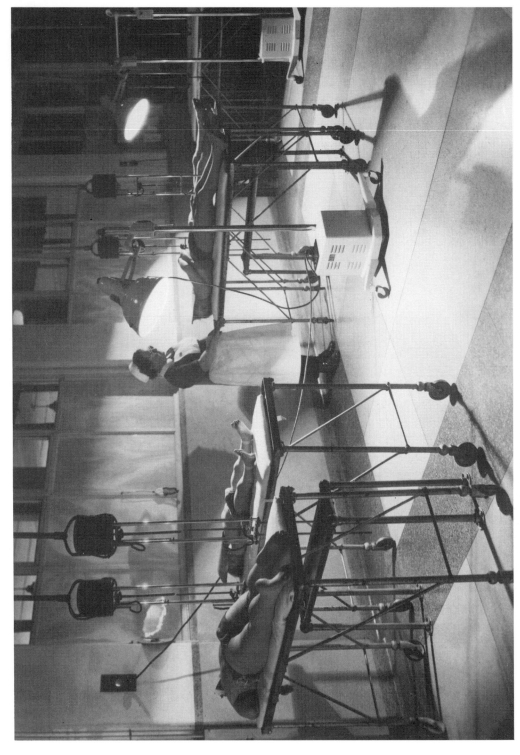

The Light Department opened by the Duke and Duchess of York in May, 1924.

Part II
1920-1948

Gauvain Knighted

Recognition came swiftly to Gauvain when in 1920, at the age of 41, he received the honour of knighthood in the New Year's Honours' List. It is no exaggeration to say that his work had led to an entirely new outlook on the part of the profession towards the possibilities of non-operative treatment of tuberculosis and the prognosis of this disease. In addition, he was the first to recognise the need for, and to provide, a Hospital school.

Gauvain's knighthood was, of course, cause for great celebrations in the Hospital and those who attended a special dinner were given permission by Gauvain to call themselves 'Honorary Treloarians'. There is at least one person still living (1988) with this title — Mr. John Sharman, a Building Officer.

The second Royal visit

On 1st July, 1922 Princess Alice, Countess of Athlone, accompanied by the Duke, visited the Hospital and named the new ambulance for transporting patients between Alton and Hayling Island – "The Athlone."

Treloar's 80th Birthday

Treloar was 80 years old on 13th January, 1923 and, despite other invitations, chose to spend the whole day (accompanied by his two adopted children, Mr. Roy and Miss Florence Treloar) with his little children at the Hospital at Alton.

The festivities started off in the dining hall where three congratulatory telegrams were read out — one each from the King, Queen Alexandra and the Princess Royal. Staff, together with young men from the College, had assembled to present Treloar with two handsome silver salvers from everyone and a 100lb. Birthday cake, complete with 80 candles, made by Adlams, Market Square, Alton.

During the festivities Gauvain read the ballad, specially written by author *C. E. Lawrence, entitled 'Bold Baronet Who Couldn't Grow Old' which ended:.

"So let us praise, as praise we can,
This fine old English gentleman".

Treloar then toured all the wards and spoke to each individual child and was pleased to autograph many a Birthday Book.

Before leaving Treloar planted a commemorative oak tree (37 on map). The festivities lasted all day and included a special lunch for the children and a staff dinner and dance that evening.

Treloar died only nine months later on 6th September, 1923. And it was said of him, "We need not mourn him — he was happy in his work."

But before his death Treloar was involved in two occasions that gave him tremendous pleasure.

Firstly, Lady Elizabeth Bowes-Lyon (now our much loved Queen Mother) was about to be married to the Duke of York. Not only did she say she would be pleased to receive a suitcase made by the Treloar College boys as a wedding gift but she invited Sir William Treloar and his adopted daughter to the presentation of this gift.

In addition, there was the unique gathering at the Hospital upon the visit of the Princess Royal.

*Not T. E. Lawrence.

Sir William Treloar cuts his birthday cake watched by Matron; in the background is smiling Miss Treloar.

The Princess Royal with Sir Henry Gauvain and Miss Robertson, followed by Sir William Treloar.

Third Royal Visit

On Founder's Day, 1923 the Hospital was honoured with a visit from The Princess Royal, accompanied by Princess Maud. As on previous Royal visits Their Royal Highnesses arrived by train at Alton Park station and were met by 'the three fathers' i.e.

The Earl of Coventry — Father of the House of Lords
Mr. T. P. O'Connor — Father of the House of Commons
Treloar — Father of the Corporation of London.

Gauvain's daughter, Suzette, presented a bouquet to The Princess Royal

Sir William Treloar with the Earl of Coventry and Mr. T. P. O'Connor, M.P.
- a unique picture of the longest serving members of the House of Lords, the
House of Commons and the Corporation of London. "The three Fathers."

and John Gauvain presented a bouquet to Princess Maud. The College
students presented each of the Princesses with a leather suitcase which they
had, of course, made themselves. Amongst those present were Sir Neville
Chamberlain.

The Princess Royal, in turn, presented each of the three 'fathers' with
horseshoes made of rosemary (for remembrance) decorated with appropriately
coloured ribbons.

The Band of the 2nd Bn. of the Royal Hampshire Regiment played
a selection of music in the grounds throughout the afternoon.

Each Princess and each of the three 'fathers' planted commemorative
trees.

The wedding gift – In April, 1923 Lady Elizabeth Bowes-Lyon (now our much loved Queen Mother) is seen here being presented with a suitcase by Treloar College boy George Perkes (who made it) as a wedding gift upon her marriage to the Duke of York. Sir William Treloar and his adopted daughter, Florence, watch the presentation. A year later the Duke and Duchess of York came to Alton.

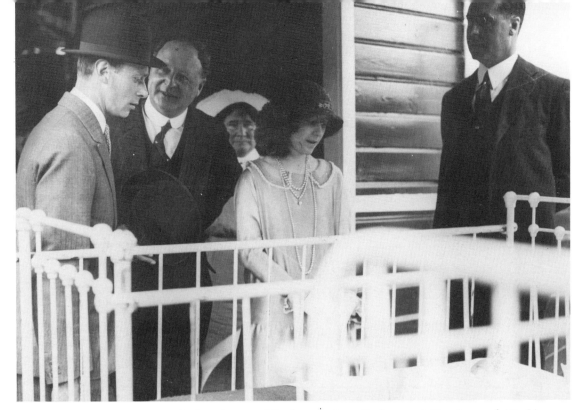

King George VI and the Queen Mother (when Duke and Duchess of York) with Sir Henry Gauvain, Dr. Jones and Miss Robertson.

Fourth Royal Visit

On Founder's Day, 30th May, 1924, the Duke and Duchess of York (now the Queen Mother) were welcomed at Alton Park station by Lord Burnham, Miss Florence Treloar, Gauvain and Miss Robertson. As before little Suzette Gauvain presented a bouquet to the Duchess.

Their Royal Highnesses opened the new Light Department, which was to do so much for the children in removing their blemishes (the aftermath of lupus vulgaris) and providing light treatment to supplement the sunlight for those with tuberculosis, as well as treating chilblains, furuncles, acne, septic conditions generally and erysipelas.

The Duke and Duchess also visited the college workshops and toured the Hospital wards, following which the Duchess presented prizes to the nurses. The Duke was presented with a pigskin suitcase made by a College boy and the Duchess with a workbasket made by the children in the Hospital.

Both the Duke and Duchess planted commemorative trees.

Throughout the day all enjoyed the music of the band of the 2nd Bn. of the Royal Hampshire Regiment.

The Queen Mother (when Duchess of York) planting a tree at Alton.

Development — 1920 to 1948

The upper age of the children in the Hospital was now extended to 14 (later 16) or, in other words, children up to school leaving age. This, in effect, helped to bridge the gap between boys being discharged from Hospital and their admission to the College.

In 1922, the British Orthopaedic Association held its Summer meeting at both Alton and Hayling Island at which Sir Robert Jones, President of the Association, recommended that Treloar be admitted as an honorary Fellow. The College boys were delighted to win a cricket match against the visiting Orthopaedic Surgeons during the course of this visit!

We now move on into an era where a great deal of what follows is in living memory. Some of the following information has been provided by Mr. John Cholmeley, Assistant Medical Officer in 1930 (later Consultant Orthopaedic Surgeon at the Royal National Orthopaedic Hospital) and some by Mr. H. H. Langston, appointed as Assistant Medical Officer in 1934

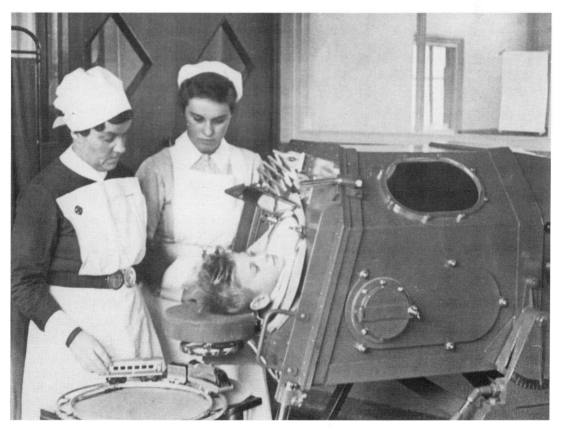

The Iron Lung.

and Surgeon in Charge (later Consultant) of all the Clinics.

Three unrelated developments occurred about this time which considerably altered the category of patients in the Hospital.

Firstly, with the passing of the Education Act in 1921 the role of the Hospital began to change. The Act made it obligatory for School Medical Officers (usually County or city Medical Officers of Health) to refer to Hospitals patients who appeared to require in-patient treatment and, in the case of children with long-term or crippling diseases, for the School Authority to pay for such treatment up to age of 18. This meant, of course, that children with tuberculosis were referred much earlier — obviously to their benefit.

Secondly, with the first poliomyelitis epidemic, admissions now began to include non—tuberculous patients. The Hospital was one of the first hospitals in the country to install an iron lung and on one occasion when the iron lung broke down members of staff spent 48 hours hand-pumping this machine in order to keep the patient alive!

Thirdly, milk was now being pasteurised with the consequent reduction of tuberculous cases. The Hospital had already installed its own pasteurisation plant.

The first Authority to act upon the terms of the 1921 Education Act was the city of Portsmouth and this led, ultimately, to the naming of one of the blocks "The Portsmouth Block".

Portsmouth not only asked for treatment of referred children (be they tuberculous or orthopaedic) in the Hospital but also suggested the setting up of an Out Patient Clinic in the City. This was agreed and a three monthly Clinic inaugurated. Mr. Fairbank, already a famous Orthopaedic Surgeon attached to King's College Hospital and Great Ormond Street, was appointed as a visiting Consultant. It soon became necessary, however, to have more frequent Clinics, which ultimately became fortnightly, and these were taken by Mr. Fairbank's Registrar. Many a patient with non-tuberculous conditions began to be admitted from other parts of the country and, indeed, Mr. Fairbank himself introduced many fascinating orthopaedic cases for full investigation.

Other Authorities quickly followed suit and clinics were established at Aldershot, Bournemouth, Fareham, Farnborough, Fordingbridge, Gosport, Winchester, Fleet, Basingstoke, Andover, Eastleigh, Totton, Newport IOW, Southampton, Havant, Camberley, Salisbury, Christchurch and Poole.

The Hospital had now opened its doors to those suffering from the skin infection, lupus vulgaris (which disease, mercifully, is not seen in Britain today). It was a most horribly disfiguring condition and could result in the destruction of the whole of the nose or ear or gross scarring of the forehead or cheek.

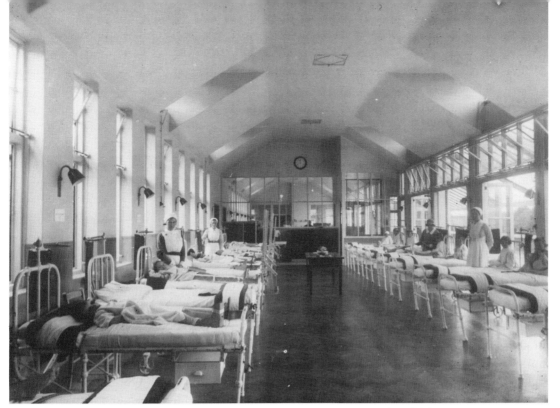

The Portsmouth Block, opened officially in 1931.

Following a visit to the Finsen Institute at Copenhagen, Gauvain installed a "Light Department". The only effective treatment available in those days was concentrated ultra violet light administered by means of the Finsen—Reyn lamp. Treatment of one child took many hours and lupus patients were under care for a long time. Obviously, after treatment, much scarring was left and this led to the invitation of Sir Harold Gillies and Mr. Pomfret Kilner (Consultant Plastic Surgeons) to join the staff in order to carry out skin grafting and transfers of skin by means of tube grafting. Sir Harold pioneered techniques for the reconstruction of the nose at the Hospital. Conditions such as repair of cleft lip and palate and ear constuctions were also undertaken.

Doctor/Parent relationship was virtually non-existent. Requests from parents to meet medical staff were rare and if such a request were made these would be conducted by junior staff. There was, however, a little doctor/parent contact at the Out Patient Department in London. Even at this clinic it by no means followed that parents were seen by Gauvain (or his deputy) as the patient was ushered into the Consulting Room whilst the parents waited in the waiting room outside. The attitude persisted during the whole of the period under review. Visiting days at the Hospital were regarded as a day off for the medical and senior nursing staff.

The medical team in 1935/36 - back row: Dr. Quibell, Mr. Binstead, Dr. Barnaby; front: Dr. Clarke, Henry Gauvain and Dr. C. E. M. Jones.

Father Christmas arrives – tremendous excitement.

Christmas was always a great occasion. Gauvain, dressed as Father Christmas, and driven by a porter dressed up as a clown, would tour the hospital in an electrically propelled trolley, distributing presents to every patient, ward by ward. In the evening all medical staff went up to Gauvain's house for an enormous Christmas dinner, presided over by Lady Gauvain and his charming daughter, Suzette. The wards were all decorated each taking a special theme i.e. "Snow White" (the faces of the dwarfs bearing a startling resemblance to the consultants!). The nurses wore fancy hats which they had made themselves, representing a song, poem etc. for which Gauvain awarded prizes. The medical staff served dinner to the nurses.

On Boxing Day morning the Hampshire Hunt then, as now, always "pays their respects" to the Hospital. The Meet is on "The Butts"; the

Father Christmas (Sir Henry Gauvain) with the domestic staff goes to the Christmas lunch – 1920's.

bitches are selected from amongst the hounds and the Hunt proceeds to the Hospital. The Hunt officials all receive a glass of cherry brandy from Matron and the Whipper-In takes selected hounds through each of the wards. Imagine - no dog is allowed in the hospital for 364 days of the year but on Boxing Day . . . ! On at least one occasion, whilst mounted, the M.F.H. deposited his empty glass on a covenient branch of a chestnut tree and - once the hunt had departed - a diminutive nurse, sent to collect the empties, was left looking up at a glass way beyond her reach! The Hunt does a couple of laps of the Hospital and it is a wonderful sight to see them in their pink coats and top hats (now mostly hard hats) with the Pony Club bringing up the rear. Most of the ponies have their tails plaited with red ribbons. Miss Geraldine Walker (Superintendant of the Physiotherapy Department) has taken part in the Hunt several times.

If the Hunt is a tradition, so also is the fancy dress hockey match held on Boxing Day afternoon between the nursing and medical staff. A Charge Nurse on one occasion is supposed to have attended on horseback dressed as a polo player bearing the placard, "If its good enough for the Duke (of Edinburgh) its good enough for me".

There must have been tremendous fun and excitement with the arrival of the Good Fairy (that wonderful personality Dr. "Jonah" Jones) with Father Christmas (Gauvain) and a junior Father Christmas (perhaps Suzette Gauvain) – early 1920's.

Father Christmas (Sir Henry Gauvain) – it was a long, long journey! (Below): the late 1940's: Father Christmas (Mr. E. Stanley Evans) with "soldier" (Mr. Cane's son) and "policeman" (Mr. Evans' son).

Founder's day 1926 was a day to remember as the Memorial Bust of Treloar on its 7 feet granite pedestal, the work of the famous sculpter Albert Toft, was unveiled by the Rt. Hon. the Viscount Cave , Lord High Chancellor. This bust stands in front of Alexandra House and is flanked by stone urns (18 on map). Lord Cave, in his speech, declared that Treloar's true monument was the work of the Hospital.

Dr. Duke-Elder was appointed in 1928 as Consultant Opthalmic Surgeon. He had made a particular study of the treatment of tuberculosis of the eye and its treatment by ultra violet light.

Facilities were now available at the Hospital for post-graduate study. The one week courses were always oversubscribed and included lectures, demonstrations and a tour of both Alton and Hayling Island. A combined Meeting of British and American Orthopaedic Associations was held at the Hospital in July, 1929.

On 5th April, 1929 the Trustees held a 21st Birthday Dinner at the Barbers' Hall, Monkwell Street, London at which an appeal was launched for £100,000 for the re-building of the Hospital. It was proposed to tackle this piecemeal, to avoid interference to the children under treatment, and as finances allowed. Commencement of the first phase was to start at once with the first Ward Block containing 60 beds.

The"News Chronicle" were instrumental in installing wirelesses in 1935. These were formally presented by Lord Mottistone, Lord Lieutenant of the County, comprising 20 loudspeakers, one for each ward, the Light Department, the School Rooms and the College. This was a most valuable adjunct not only for pleasure but for the educational programmes. Three years later when lessons were actually broadcast to supplement oral work this was immediately seized upon to widen the patients' horizons.

At about this time the orthopaedic work of the Hospital increased in scope, i.e.

(a) treatment of the early patterns of paralysis and deformity resulting from poliomyelitis, spastic paralysis etc.

(b) treatment of congenital deformities.

(c) treatment of non-tuberculous bone and joint infections.

(d) repair of injuries, accidents and burns.

(e) muscular dystrophies.

1929 – with due Masonic ceremony, the Rt. Hon. Lord Ampthill (M. W. Pro Branch Master of the United Grand Lodge of England) laid the foundation stone . . .

The New Buildings

The foundation stone was laid on 22nd October, 1929 with Masonic ceremonial by the Rt. Hon. Lord Ampthill, Most Worshipful Pro Grand Master of the United Grand Lodge of England. Lord Ampthill struck each of the four corners of the foundation stone with a maul used in Egypt 4,000 years previously. Papers were placed within a phial and the phial, in turn, placed in a cavity within the stone, after which a plate was placed over the cavity. Connaught Block was the first to be built and was in use by 5th December, 1930. This ward was named after Princess Arthur of Connaught, President of the Queen Alexandra League.

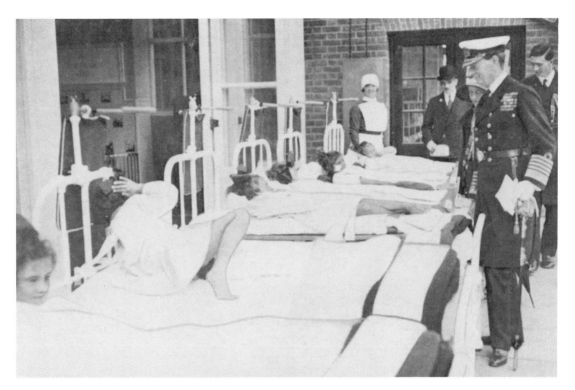

Founder's Day, 1931 – Admiral Sir Roger Keynes talking to young patients.

Portsmouth Block was opened by Admiral of the Fleet, Sir Roger Keynes, C-in-C Portsmouth on Founder's Day 1931. As promised the names of the officers and men who fell in the Battle of Jutland were now permanently recorded on tablets placed in this ward. Admiral Keynes was handed a commemorative key by Miss Treloar to mark the occasion.

As the Princess Arthur of Connaught was unable to be present to perform the official opening ceremony of The Princess Royal Block, her sister, Lady Maude Carnegie, deputised and unveiled two name tablets on 30th June, 1932.

A new kitchen block and dining room were built for nursing and domestic staff and in addition a new Isolation ward (later Burnham Ward) was added.

During these excavations Roman remains were found.

Founder's Day, 1935 – Marquis and Marchioness of Reading laying the foundation stone of the Silver Jubilee Treatment Centre.

Founder's Day, 1935 had an even greater significance because the occasion was marked by the laying of the foundation stone for the new Silver Jubilee Treatment Centre by the Marquis of Reading. The Treatment Block was the most important building of the reconstructed Hospital and comprised, inter alia:-

a modern operating theatre
a recovery room
X-ray Department
Electro Therapeutic Treatment Room
Waiting room

Opposite: Nursing staff, 1935/36.

Many visitors came down from London with Lord and Lady Reading and a Guard of Honour of College boys lined the path from Alton Park station to the marquee which was erected around the stone. Gauvain then placed in a cavity of the foundation stone a glass phial containing a Jubilee coin, a programme of the ceremony, the annual report of the Hospital and a newspaper of the day, the whole being bound with red, white and blue bunting.

Lord Reading was presented with a suitcase by Patrick Keane (a boy from both Hospital and College) and examples of tapestry work from a girl in-patient of the Hospital, as mementoes.

The Treatment Centre was, in fact, a living memorial to King George V, who had died in 1936. Shortly afterwards Lord Reading also died and Lady Reading kindly returned the silver ceremonial trowel to the Hospital where it can be seen in the Library.

Today it seeems amazing how rapidly these buildings were erected and put into commision.

When British lawn tennis star Dorothy Round was the guest of honour at one of the nurses' prize-givings at the Hospital, the nurses persuaded her to give them some tennis tips.

An aerial view of the new Hospital buildings.

Two views of the new buildings opened by the Duke of Kent in 1937.

Sixth Royal Visit

On 10th June, 1937 the Duke of Kent visited the Silver Jubilee Treatment Centre and was welcomed by the Chairman of the Trustees, Colonel the Hon. Frederick Lawson, who invited him to open the new buildings of the Hospital.

Afterwards the Duke inspected the Hospital wards, the Hospital School and the College Workshops.

College boy Douglas Hayward on his way to Buckingham Palace to present a suitcase, made by him and other Treloar College boys, to the Duke of Kent on the occasion of his marriage.

1938-9 – the occasion; the monthly visit to the Hospital of Professor Kilner. With him are (left to right): Dr. Jones, Dr. Hunter, of St. Bartholomew's Hospital, Prof. Kilner, Dr. Butler, Mr. H. H. Langston.

Resignation of Miss Janet Robertson

Miss Robertson resigned on 1st February, 1936 and her great popularity was well illustrated by a ceremony on her retirement when, after farewell gifts, it was suggested to her that she should make a triumphal drive around the Hospital. This was accompanied by such loud cheering that it had to be repeated a second time. All ambulant patients and all nursing and medical staff lined the terrace with the children's beds pushed as near as possible in order to get a better view. Miss Robertson was driven around at a slow, royal pace with her head out of the window, waving farewell.

Her greatest reward must have been the number of children she had nursed over the years.

After her death in November, 1952, a plaque to her memory was installed in the chapel.

The Second World War

"To meet the Government's request for economy of paper etc. a full annual report of the Hospital is not being published during the war but only essential accounts and statistics" — signed Florence Treloar, Acting Chairman..

Consequently, comparatively little was recorded about the Hospital during the war years. Transport was difficult. Small, weak children had to be transported by public transport over considerable distances with reduced services and inconvenient connections. There was a paper shortage. Fewer visits were made by Hon. Consulting staff. There was a slight decrease in the number of patients admitted owing to:

Medical Staff shortage;

Nursing shortage (many careers were now open to women and fewer were applying for nursing);

Added increase of infectious diseases during Winter months;

Shortage of domestic staff;

Few able-bodied men available for portering which had to be done by very young or elderly men.

The shortage of staff was somewhat alleviated by the arrival of German P.O.W.s who came to help.

The Hospital school was busy knitting for the Merchant Navy and they also made garments for their own use. Several groups of children adopted British Prisoners of War through the Red Cross and sent five shillings each month for parcels.

A pleasant event took place at Christmas, 1943 with the unexpected visit by a party of 100 American airmen bringing sweets and presents for the children in the Hospital.

Food, as always, was provided from the Hospital gardens. The Hospital also produced all its own poultry, eggs, pigs and so on. Patients, in fact, did well on war time rationing, presumably because of the low fat content.

An Anderson shelter was built in Alexandra woods but the Hospital itself escaped unscathed. Not so the Out Patient Clinics in London and Southampton, both of which were bombed in 1941. With the loss of the former, most of the Hospital records were gone for ever.

Lady Gauvain continued to run the X-Ray Department and when Suzette Gauvain qualified in 1943 she was employed as a Houseman.

There remained only a very few private tuberculosis patients in the huts in the grounds of Morland Hall (now the site of Ashdell Estate, Alton). The main house was filled from 1940 to the end of the war by children from a Belgian Hospital. They had arrived by boat and train via Portsmouth together with an entire Catholic Order of Nuns, their Mother Superior and their Priest.

Gauvain's Death

Gauvain was suffering from a neurological condition and developed bilateral lower limb paralysis the cause of which was never fully explained. He walked with the aid of two sticks but still managed to drive. Unfortunately on 6th June, 1944, he fell and fractured his hip. The fracture was reduced and internally fixed by V. H. Ellis. He was kept in Hospital for some two to three months, after which he was sent to his own private clinic, Morland Hall, where he had a bed in his drawing room. Despite his immobility, Gauvain used to attend the Hospital about twice a week in order to see the Hospital Secretary, Stanley Cane. This was organised by his valet and his chauffeur who put a naval 'hammock' in Gauvain's wheelchair by which means they were able to hoist him onto the back seat of one of his Daimlers (he had two — one grey — one black). Despite treatment, and because of progressive complications, he became bed ridden and died in January 1945. An excerpt from his Obituary reads:

"A man of great personal charm, he was able to arouse affection and loyalty in his staff. . . . An apostle of conservatism in an era which has seen the greater part of the development and elaboration of orthopaedic operative technique, Gauvain's contribution to orthopaedic surgery is perhaps greater than is at present realised. To those who knew him, he will long remain a friend and mentor whose wisdom, kindliness and humour will not be forgotten."

A memorial service was held in St. Bartholomews The Great, London on 2nd February, 1945. His ashes were sent to Alderney where he was born.

His portrait, painted by Mr. Frank Salisbury and unveiled by the President of the Royal College of Surgeons, is in the waiting room of the Silver Jubilee Treatment Centre, and a ward, the Library and one of the College Houses are named after him.

Dr. Jones' Death

Gauvain was succeeded by Dr. C. E. M. Jones ('Jonah'), his Deputy, who had been working in the Hospital for 26 years.

He took over as Medical Superintendent in January, 1945 but, sadly died on 3rd August, 1945.

For over quarter of a century he had laboured unobtrusively in the Hospital amongst the children he loved. His personality was ideally suited to that of his Chief to whom he gave unswerving loyalty. His dry wit and genial hospitality attracted and cemented many a friendship. By his untimely death the Hospital and children suffered a grevious loss.

PART III

1948-1968

The Appointment of
Mr. E. Stanley Evans CBE, MB, BS, FRCS.

Stanley Evans' two main interests were the clinical care of orthopaedic conditions in children and adolescents and the training and welfare of the disabled which made him eminently suitable to replace Gauvain in 1946.

During the years of Evans' term as Superintendent the nature of the work of the Hospital changed yet again. The introduction of anti-tuberculous chemotherapy, streptomycin and poliomyelitis immunisation resulted in a vast reduction of patients with severe disabling disease and enabled the Hospital to extend its care to children with congenital deformities and adults with various musculo-skeletal disabilities.

The National Health Service took over the Hospital in 1948; the College, however, decided to remain an independent institution and moved to a large and beautiful Elizabethan house in Froyle. The post of the Medical Superintendent, therefore, became defunct and Evans continued as the senior Consultant Orthopaedic Surgeon; he subsequently became a Trustee of the Governing Body of the College and its Chairman in 1966. He retired in 1968 and his appointment as Chairman of the Hospital was taken over by John A. Wilkinson.

It was typical of Evans' vision that he inaugurated special provision for the care and treatment of haemophiliacs. His contribution to the welfare of the disabled was recognised in 1951 by the award of the CBE.

Personalities . . .

Sir Henry Gauvain, MD, MChir(Cantab), MD (Hon) Melb. FRCS, JP

Gauvain was born in Alderney of an old Channel Island family. He qualified at St Bartholomew's Hospital and was appointed to Treloar Hospital, Alton in 1908 at the age of 29 years.

He was married to a Sister, also from St Bartholomew's Hospital, who was a great help to Gauvain throughout his career. She ran the Hospital's X-Ray Department for years. They lived in the Medical Superintendent's house (item 27 on map). They had one daughter, Suzette.

Gauvain was a man of great personal charm. He was able to arouse affection and loyalty in his staff. He was also a man of action and of great administrative ability — always ready to listen to, and discuss suggestions from, his staff. Once a decision was arrived at, it was adhered to and pursued unswervingly. He had a faculty of keeping his children happy and this was exemplified by the way in which his essential kindness and greatness of heart won the affection and secured the contentment of his children and adult patients at his private clinic at Morland Hall, Alton. He was a gifted speaker with a pleasing and lively manner.

He was also a local Justice of the Peace.

Sir Henry would arrive at Morland Hall at 10.30 every morning. He would sit at his desk in the blue drawing room and go through his mail, after which he would give instructions for dinner and how many guests to expect. When he had finished his correspondence he would consult with Dr. D. Macrae ("Jock" his Registrar at Morland Hall — later orthopaedic consultant at the Hospital) and then leave for the Hospital, returning again at 7.00 p.m. for dinner at Morland Hall.

Dr. Charles E. M. Jones, BA, MB, BC
('Jonah')
Assistant Medical Officer

Dr. Jones had been in General Practice as a junior partner with his father before World War I. At an early stage in that war he was a member of the Army which invaded Southern Iraq and reached as far as the city of Kut where the whole Army was humiliatingly defeated and forced to surrender. As a result Dr. Jones became a Prisoner of War at Coutte in Turkey for something over three years. The conditions of the Prisoners of War camps were apparently appalling; the prisoners were all suffering from chronic intestinal infection with totally inadequate drugs available for such disease and when he was released, he was in a very poor state of health.

Dr. Jones thus welcomed the offer of a permanent appointment at the Hospital whose staff he joined in 1919 as Assistant Medical Officer, becoming, later, Deputy Superintendent and remaining in this office until Gauvain's death in 1945. The rôle of Deputy Medical Superintendent was one that Dr. Jones fulfilled admirably. He had no personal ambition for any personal advancement but very thoroughly enjoyed, and conscientiously carried out, his duties in this rôle and, indeed, as a clinician became very expert in the conservative management of tuberculous disease.

He had a wonderful and wicked sense of humour and an amazing memory. He was a great raconteur. On occasions, when asked, he was a witty public speaker and had a lot to do with maintaining morale and pride in the reputation of the Hospital. He was (rightly or wrongly) regarded as Gauvain's shadow but, in fact, carried out a rôle as 'peacemaker' and smoothed things down.

Amongst his many other abilities was a great dramatic skill and he succeeded in persuading the most unlikely junior to take part in the annual Hospital Dramatic Entertainment, revealing skills they did not know they possessed.

Dr. Jones was a large, bespectacled gentleman who lived in the Resident Medical Officers' bungalow (item 23 on map). He was accompanied everywhere he went by a large airedale called 'Old Moll'. Apparently he used to feed her by means of throwing food to her from their meal table, including things like rice pudding! Jonah presided at all meals in the bungalow which boasted two well-organised little maids referred to as 'Winnetts' by Jonah. Free beer was provided by courtesy of Courages in Alton.

Jonah would also administer anaesthetics. He had a shrewd clinical sense and had an enviable turn of phrase i.e. when doing some unpleasant task he would say, "It is my melancholy pleasure . . ."

Dr. Jones

On 6th May, 1939, at a dinner at the Swan Hotel, Alton to commemorate his twenty years' service, Jonah was presented with a beautiful silver plaque upon which was engraved 37 signatures of the staff of the Hospital.

No Treloar and Gauvain Dining Club Annual Dinner is ever complete without at least one story of Jonah's exploits.

Jonah, on Gauvain's death in 1945, took over as Medical Superintendent of the Hospital but only for eight months as he himself developed a perforated ulcer and was operated on by Mr. Mortimer Woolf (a visiting consultant) but, alas, too late to save Jonah's life.

Sir Thomas Fairbank, DSO, OBE, MS, FRCS, Hon. M.Ch. (Orth)

Fairbank was a famous orthopaedic surgeon attached to King's College Hospital and the Hospital for Sick Children at Great Ormond Street.

He operated at Treloar Hospital once a fortnight. He was a superb technician and would work all day no matter how many cases there were. He would arrive about 8 a.m. and go to the Residents' Bungalow for breakfast and then work until about 9 p.m. when everyone was 'flaked out'. He was very particular and everyone assisting in theatre would have to scrub up for ten minutes by the watch. On one occasion Fairbank forgot the time and everyone had to scrub up a second time. Carefulness and neatness were the essence of all Fairbank's operative procedures and he was a great believer in the 'no touch' technique. He would admit some of his London patients to the Hospital who were of special interest. He took over the responsibility of the clinic at Portsmouth and for many years visited it once in three months and even up to the outbreak of World War II he was paying at least an annual visit to see patients of special interest.

Fairbank was a typical example of all the best aspects of Victorian courtesy and he had a delightfully dry sense of humour. He was, however, handicapped very early in life by severe deafness. He was a very kind man who never said a bad word about anyone. The only way he would show his disapproval was whilst sitting in the front row of the Royal Society of Medicine, if he did not agree with what was going on, there was a loud click as he turned off the switch at the top of his enormous hearing aid.

Professor E. W. Hey Groves, MD, MS, FRCS (1872-1944)

In 1917 Professor Hey Groves helped to found the Association of British Orthopaedic Surgeons. At that time he was in surgical charge of the Military Orthopaedic Hospital at Bristol. He became successively Editor of 'The British Journal of Surgery' Vice-President of the Royal College of Surgeons, President of the British Orthopaedic Association and President of the Association of Surgeons (a dual honour). He was promoted to the Chair of Surgery at Bristol in 1922.

1946 – Farewell to Sir Thomas Fairbank.
At the back: Unknown, Mr. H. H. Langston, Mr. Stanley Evans, (?) Mr.
Macrae; front: Sister Cole, Miss Walker Matron, Sir Thomas Fairbank, Dr.
Suzette Gauvain, Sister Smith.

Hey Groves was invited to join the staff of the Hospital by Gauvain as a result of a friendship which developed whilst both found themselves on a long holiday cruise (it is thought to the West Indies) in about 1935.

Hey Groves made fortnightly visits to the Hospital. He brought many cases with him from Bristol to be treated in the Hospital which was of value to the young surgeon in training.

The complete opposite of Sir Thomas Fairbank, Hey Groves was full of vitality, had a prodigious memory and a rumbustious sense of humour.

His visits were day long. He would overnight in Alton and arrive at the Hospital at 8.30 a.m. in order to begin his ward rounds. He was an excellent teacher. After an early lunch his operative session would start — finishing by about 5 p.m. He was usually accompanied by his wife and his secretary who made copious notes during both his round and his operative session.

Mr. H. Heber Langston, MB, BS, FRCS

Heber Langston was trained at St Bartholomew's Hospital and was appointed as an assistant to Sir Henry Gauvain in 1934. During the early years of his appointment, before the Second World War, he assisted Sir Henry Gauvain, Sir Thomas Fairbank and Professor Ernest Hey Groves. Few people could claim a better training in elective orthopaedic surgery, having worked for masters in the management of skeletal tuberculosis, poliomyelitis and congenital and acquired deformities in children.

During the war years he worked additionally at the E.M.S. (Emergency Medical Service) Hospital at Basingstoke, together with V. H. Ellis, and dealt with a large number of D-Day casualties. After the war, he was appointed to the Royal South Hants Hospital and was the first orthopaedic surgeon appointed to Southampton. In 1952 he was also appointed to the Royal Hampshire County Hospital and worked there with James Ellis (later Professor James Ellis of Southampton University) until 1971, following which he concentrated his sessions on the new teaching hospital in Southampton General and the Lord Mayor Treloar Hospital.

During his career, he was appointed as a member of the South West Metropolitan Board and later the Wessex Regional Hospital Board and in 1971 became Chairman of the Medical Advisory Committee. He also served on the management committees of Southampton Hospitals and the Lord Mayor Treloar Hospital. He was appointed to the Central Health Services Council, and served on it until it was abolished.

In 1949, he became a Hampshire County Councillor and stood as an Independent for seven years. In 1949 he was appointed to the Council of the B.M.A. in London serving 18 years and was Chairman of the Central Hospital Medical Service for 12 years. In 1971, he was appointed Vice-President of the B.M.A.

He retired from the National Health Service in 1972 and was invited to the Chair of Orthopaedics in the Medical College of the University of Baghdad. He served as its Professor for $3\frac{1}{2}$ years.

His main contribution to orthopaedic surgery was that of an administrator, not only to his local hospitals but also nationwide. He played a rôle in the establishment of the Southampton University Medical School and continued his interest in children's orthopaedics until he retired.

H. H. Langston

Mr. Stanley Cane

Stanley Cane began his career in Hospital administration at King's College, London and in 1935 worked for the Hospital in their London offices at Ely Place.

With the outbreak of World War II the office staff moved to Alton where he, his wife and baby son moved into No. 1 Farm Cottage (34 on map) with Dr. Kenneth Butler living next door. On Mr. Harper's retirement, Mr. Cane took over as Hospital Secretary in 1943. By 1946, Mr. Cane's family having increased, they moved to the Bungalow (24 on map) where they remained until his retirement in 1969. The Bungalow has only recently been demolished.

Mr Cane was always kind, courteous and very approachable. He it was who organised the venue, menu and wines for the Treloar and Gauvain Dining Club each year.

Mr. Donald E. Macrae ('Jock'), MB, BS, FRCS

Macrae was trained at St. Bartholomew's Hospital (indeed it was said that if one had not trained at this particular hospital there was no hope of being employed at Alton) and was appointed by Gauvain as his Resident Surgical Officer at Morland Hall, his wife, Janet, being the Matron.

When he married Janet, Langston was his Best Man and, indeed, the Macrae's started off their married life in Langston's house in Alton.

When Gauvain died, Macrae continued in his work, as Dr. Ronald Murray and his wife Suzette had taken over the running of the Clinic. Because of the long stay of the patients Macrae knew each one individually and was familiar with all their problems.

Eventually Morland Hall was transferred to the care of the Wessex Regional Hospital Board. A lack of patients with skeletal tuberculosis enforced its closure in 1953. It was agreed that Macrae should be given sessions and beds at Treloar's and the Royal South Hants. Hospital at Southampton. He continued as an expert in chronic bone infections and also retrained as an Accident Surgeon. He was made a Fellow of the British Orthopaedic Association in 1968, but died in 1977.

Dr. C. J. Suzette Gauvain, MA, MRCP, FFCM, FFOM, DPH, DIH

Suzette Gauvain first met Ronald Murray in 1936. They would probably have got engaged in 1939 but in those days no House Surgeon could afford to marry. Dr. Murray joined the Army in 1939 and because he was on active service he was, in fact, allowed to marry Suzette in July 1940. In his Will, Gauvain left Morland Hall to his daughter. Suzette and her husband ran it jointly for adult tuberculous patients for various County Councils. It was then renamed Gauvain Hospital.

House staff were difficult to obtain during the war, so Gauvain, the moment his daughter had qualified in 1943, seized the opportunity to employ her as a Medical Officer in the Hospital. She took over the responsibility of Hayling Island when it re-opened. In addition she helped with anaesthetics for Sir Thomas Fairbank's list. Unfortunately Sir Thomas was extremely deaf and when Suzette told him, during an operation, that Mr. Pomfret Kilner (the Plastic Surgeon) had recently been awarded the C.B.E., Fairbank was heard to reply, "Poor Kilner — at his time of life: fancy getting a TB knee!"

After four years in the Lebanon where she taught at the American University Hospital, she returned to England in 1958 and became very interested in occupational medicine, becoming Deputy Director, Employment Medical Advisory Service. She held many honorary appointments one of which was a Governor of the Treloar Trust. She died in 1980.

Dr. Ronald O. Murray, MBE, MD(Cantab), MB, BCh., MRCP, DMR

Son-in-law of Gauvain, he was asked to go over to the Hospital occasionally, from Morland Hall, to report on X-Rays and was finally asked to join the staff as Radiological Registrar in May 1948 just before the introduction of the N.H.S. Shortly afterwards he was appointed as Consultant at Heatherwood Hospital, Ascot and the Royal National Orthopaedic Hospitals.

In 1954 he and Suzette went to Beirut for four years and Murray became the Associate Professor of Radiology.

He returned to U.K. and rapidly gained National and International recognition as an expert in bone radiology and contributed to the post-graduate meetings held at the Hospital. He was eventually appointed as an Honorary Lecturer to the new Southampton University Medical School and played a major rôle in the post-graduate training of Radiological Senior Registrars in the region.

He retired in 1984 and was succeeded by Dr. Graham Plant.

Mr. E. Stanley Evans, CBE, MB, BS, FRCS

Evans qualified at St. Bartholomew's Hospital, London in 1927. He married Muriel Henderson (herself a doctor) in 1930 and became successively Medical Superintendent of Heatherwood Hospital, Ascot and Queen Mary's Hospital for Children, Carshalton and, whilst keeping the latter appointment, took over as Medical Superintendent at Treloar Hospital in 1946.

It was said of him that "his was a great gift of making the despondent and discouraged believe in themselves and of matching disability to ability".

Evans was one of the few who linked a comprehensive knowledge of the needs of all ages with the skills of the orthopaedic surgeon. He was a warm-hearted, friendly man, capable of inspiring enthusiasm in those with whom he worked and who had an infinity of concern and patience in listening to the cares and anxieties of the disabled.

Evans was also an excellent speaker playing no small part at public meetings in putting the needs of the disabled before the public in a characteristically vivid way.

At private gatherings amongst colleagues his dry humour and range of anecdotes, especially when related in a Welsh dialect, were a true delight.

Mr and Mrs Evans and their five sons lived, of course, in the Medical Superintendent's house in the Hospital and could be seen on a Sunday morning playing tennis on their own private grass tennis court.

Mr. John Wilkinson, BSc., MB, MCh., FRCS

John Wilkinson received his postgraduate orthopaedic training in the Royal National Orthopaedic Hospital, the Hospital for Sick Children, Great Ormond Street, and the Westminster Hospital, during which time he held a research appointment at the Institute of Orthopaedics in Child Health. His research into the aetiology of congenital dislocation of the hip was recognised by the award of the Robert Jones Gold Medal in 1960 and a Hunterian Professorship in 1962. He visited orthopaedic centres in North America as a Travelling Fellow in 1962.

In 1964, he was appointed to the Southampton Hospitals and the Wessex Regional Hospital Board and in 1966 he succeeded Mr. Heber Langston as the Consultant in Paediatric Orthopaedics at the Lord Mayor Treloar Hospital. He brought his experiences in children's work to that hospital and established a new surgical programme for the treatment of children with congenital dislocation of the hip. During the past 20 years, more than

600 children have been treated for this condition as well as many other children disabled by congenital or acquired deformities of their limbs.

In 1972, he was joined by Mr Robert Jackson, who has specialised in the treatment of children's spinal conditions, including scoliosis, and in 1988 Mr. Nicholas Clarke was appointed to the staff of the hospital to help with the increasing demand of children's orthopaedic care.

Miss Florence Treloar's 80th Birthday

The Hospital presented a brilliant scene on 26th April, 1949 when Miss Treloar planted a flowering cherry tree in the grounds to celebrate her 80th Birthday.

Before the ceremony an informal lunch took place at which senior members of the staff were present and Miss Treloar was presented with a bouquet of carnations tied with the ribbon of the Queen Alexandra League of which she had been Vice-President for many years.

Later the same day Miss Treloar was entertained to tea at a large gathering and she cut her Birthday cake on which were 80 candles. Mr. Evans referred to the great personal interest Miss Treloar had taken in the children over the last 40 years and the kindness and understanding she had always shown in the welfare of the staff — remembering her own nursing days no doubt. Mr. Evans also referred to her work as a Trustee (the only woman) and how she had shown firmness and determination to see what she considered right, in the interests of the Hospital, was carried out.

Miss Treloar visited each ward and was overwhelmed with little posies and gifts presented to her by the small children. The day ended with a dance in Beech House.

The above afternoon and evening programmes were repeated the following day to enable all the staff to attend on a split shift basis.

Miss Treloar's 80th birthday. In front of the Founder's statue are Miss Jeannie Walker (Matron), Sister Brown (Deputy Matron), Miss Treloar, and Dr. Suzette Gauvain (Mrs. Ronald Murray). Photograph: Edwin Plomer, Alton.

Development — 1948-1968

As a result of the National Health Service Act, the Hospital was taken over by the Ministry of Health in 1948 and its management passed from the hands of the Trustees into those of the Hospital Management Committee who were responsible to the South West Metropolitan Regional Hospital Board. Morland Hall was also taken over by the N.H.S. and renamed Gauvain Hospital. For several years it housed patients from the Channel Islands who had so recently suffered deprivation during the German occupation. Gauvain Hospital finally closed in 1953, the patients being transferred to Treloar Hospital.

In 1951 adult patients were admitted. The oldest patient had her 101st birthday a few weeks after she was admitted with a fractured femur which was successfully treated by surgical reduction. The adult patients settled in just as happily as the children.

The Hospital was, once again, renamed as the 'Lord Mayor Treloar Orthopaedic Hospital'. Most of the Trustees became members of the Hospital Management Committee of which Lord Burnham was Chairman.

With the population explosion in Basingstoke the Cottage Hospital at Hackwood Road was no longer able to cope with the increased number of patients. As a temporary measure, therefore, Treloar Hospital provided beds for General Surgery, Gynaecology and Medicine in addition to a local Casualty Service. It became the nucleus of the new Basingstoke District Hospital.

In 1958 the Alton Group was formed which included Treloar Hospital and Alton General Hospital. Three years later the Alton Group merged with the Winchester Group which then became the North Hampshire Group Hospital Management Committee. When the Groups merged, some of the surgical and medical work which had hitherto taken place at Alton General Hospital, was transferred to Treloar Hospital.

The first total hip replacements recorded at the Hospital were undertaken in about 1967.

Two celebrities visited the Hospital at about this time. The first was Frank Sinatra who paid a private visit in order to see a friend of his who was an in-patient in the Hospital. He arrived by helicopter which landed in the field, where the Sports Centre now stands, there he was met by a chauffeur driven car and also by Stanley Cane, the Hospital Secretary. The second was Wilfrid Pickles, who, together with his wife Mabel 'at the table' and Miss Violet Carson 'at the piano' conducted one of their radio programmes, 'Have a Go' in the wards on Christmas Day which was very popular.

Miss Walker the Matron, Sister Hadley, Mabel and Wilfrid Pickles (Photograph: Robert Small, Alton).

The Hospital, by the end of the 1960s, was on a slippery downward slope (see chart). The College had departed; children, fortunately, were rarely admitted with tuberculosis or poliomyelitis; hip, shoulder and knee replacements had barely begun and the non-orthopaedic cases in the Hospital were shortly due to be transferred to the new Basingstoke Mini Hospital. It was time to re-assess the future of the Hospital as a Specialist Orthopaedic Centre.

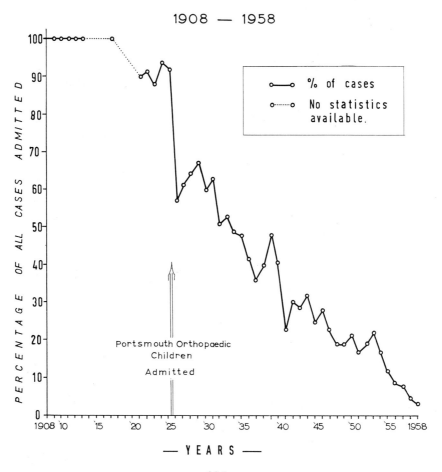

LORD MAYOR TRELOAR ORTHOPAEDIC HOSPITAL
TOTAL (NON - PULMONARY) TUBERCULOSIS ADMISSIONS
1908 — 1958

'Camelot' (1960s)

There might be a shadow lurking over the future of the Hospital in the 1960s but a nurses production of 'Camelot' was still great fun.

A Whit Monday barbecue for the student nurses of the 1960 (Photograph: Rob Small). But there was a lot of studying to be done. (Below) The Library in the Nurses' Training School.

Lord Mayor Treloar College

The Early Days

The College was founded (in conjunction with the Hospital) for young men aged between 14 and 18 years (i.e. at the completion of their statutory education) — to quote Treloar's own words:
"for patients who can either be satisfactorily treated in a hospital or else did not lend themselves to treatment, save from an educational point of view. They are deformed and thereby severely handicapped in the struggle for existence; their general health is, as a rule, good and not materially affected, with a few exceptions, by their disease. The obviously helpful way of dealing with them was on the educational side. For lads under these conditions I devised my College."

The youngsters had to have the full use of both hands.

The aim of the College, under the direction of Mr. Salt, was to give such technical instruction to disabled youngsters, whose disability could not be alleviated, to enable them to earn their own living and to "give them a 'manly tone' and teach them not to whine over their physical defects but to face the battle of life with confidence and courage."

Youngsters arrived by train at Alton Park in a state of apathy, undernourished, ill, poorly clothed and from wretched homes. Their outlook was warped and to them the future held very little prospect. Skilled, tactful training, good diet, recreation and hobbies quickly effected a change however.

On arrival the pupils were assessed as to:
(a) the amount of work he was able to do.
(b) the nature of the work best suited to him (i.e. those with active tuberculosis were given outside work such as horticulture).
(c) their future management in hospital with regard to their specific disease.

In addition, therefore, to his technical training, the pupil would receive physiotherapy, massage and/or "drill" with dumb bells as well as playing team games.

Accommodation (33 on first map) was provided for between 40 and 60 young men and consisted of:

School House   — containing 2 large dormitories and 25 small cubicles
Technical School — Carpenter's Shop —
                    where splints and crutches were made for the Hospital
                    (later managed by an old College boy Mr. Ware, and
                    5 assistants (also from the College))

	— Leather Workshop —
	making bags of all descriptions, fitted cases, portmandeaux, travelling bags, belts, purses, boots for themselves, boot and shoe repairs (the latter particularly for those who could only work sitting down).
	— Tailoring Workshop —
	where from 1915 they made all their own uniforms – khaki serge suits, blue serge overcoats – and nurses cloaks
Concert Room 50′ square	— for games, music, plays etc.
Library	
Mansion House Museum	— to house their Natural History specimens and curios
Basement under Main Ward Block	— where the youngsters made surgical boots, bound splints with leather as required and finished off celluloid splints for the Hospital.

The cost to the inmates was £15 per annum payable in advance for boys sent by parents and friends or philanthropic Societies but the Trustees had power to reduce this in case of need. The young people also had to pay their way to Alton and provide sufficient to cover their return fare.

The cubicles were allocated to monitors who had earned this by good behaviour and industry. One or two of the cubicles were allotted, for health reasons, when it was considered wise to separate a pupil from the rest. Each young man had to make his own bed and scrub the floor of his own cubicle. Those living in the dormitory were divided into "squads" and had to do the scrubbing in turns.

In 1909, as previously mentioned, a poultry farm, piggeries and a market garden were established in the Hospital grounds and it is recorded that small pigs were sent to Basingstoke market and sold for the price of £3.8s.0d. each. In the same year the poultry farm produced 12,000 eggs.

Although new entrants were supposed to have received general education up to the age of 14, in the early days at least, many young men arrived at Alton completely illiterate or with very little previous education (for whatever reason).

It was thus decided to start a College School. This was run, initially, by the Hospital School Mistress and consisted of as little as 1½ hours instruction per day. Later more subjects were undertaken including Natural History and Religious Instruction (as in the Hospital and Hospital School according to the religious faith of the parent) and the teaching duties were handed over to a schoolmaster which he combined with the general supervision of the College. This tuition was of great assistance, giving the

The Tailoring Workshop.

The College's original Leather Workshop.

boys a new interest and improving the practical work which they were undertaking in the various workshops.

In 1915 the College received an order from the War Office to provide, within eight weeks, 24,000 Army greatcoat straps. The boys were delighted to be taking an active part in the war effort and wanted to abandon their cricket matches on Saturday afternoons in order to devote extra time to their war work!

The College was run on almost military lines with "Réveille" sounding at 6.30 a.m. and "Lights Out" at 9.30 p.m. To some extent this was probably necessary as few pupils had experienced anything approaching discipline and did not know what it was to have a structure to the day.

Once a month Gauvain carried out an inspection of all the College boys and at this inspection he liked as many of the Medical staff as possible also to be present. The Headmaster gave personal reports about the general and educational progress of each boy before he entered the room. The young man was then ushered in — entirely naked apart from footwear — and this, most found extremely embarrassing. (This custom was continued by Stanley Evans as recently as 1968). Their disability, obviously, was examined but if they had received an unfavourable report from the Headmaster, then they were reproved at the same time . . . !

In order to broaden their outlook, the students were taken to the Zoo, football matches, an old Roman Fort, Bertram Mills Circus, Richboro Castle, Aldershot Tattoo, Aldershot Leather Tannery, British Industries Fair etc. They had their own Scout Troop and, indeed, received a visit from Sir Robert Baden-Powell (as he then was) the World Chief Scout who presented badges to 30 boys. (Sir Robert then lived at Bentley).

Other activities included such things as keeping their own pets i.e. rabbits, guinea pigs and white mice for which they made the hutches etc. from 'miscellaneous materials', football and cricket matches, concerts and plays, singing, badminton, woodwork and metal work and, as previously mentioned, "drill" with dumb bells.

First mention of an Old Boys' Association is in 1920 since when these have been annual events (and still are). There are innumerable success stories which was, and is, encouraging. One young man actually pushed his hand-propelled wheelchair 120 miles from Rugby to Alton in order to attend the Reunion. Old Boys would visit the College frequently for a friendly game of cricket. Contributions to the Hospital were received from the Old Boys' Association and a tablet commemorating these gifts will be found in the main hall of the Silver Jubilee Treatment Centre.

Leather goods were exhibited by the College boys at the 'Daily Express' Woman's Exhibition at Olympia, in 1922.

It can truly be said that the College was a great success. Up to 18 young men 'passed out' each year fully qualified in their particular trade;

The College boys in the classroom and at drill in the early days of the College.

the Trust provided each of them with a set of tools of their trade in order to give them a start in life and this is still done today if the need can be justified. When Treloar died in 1923 no fewer than 400 boys had passed through the College and nearly all of these had either gained open employment or established themselves in their own businesses. However, arising from the latter, experience showed that one of the most serious drawbacks from which the young people of the College suffered on leaving to commence work, was the lack of knowledge of business principles, particularly when setting up a business of their own. In order to remedy this, classes were held three evenings per week when the youngsters received instructions in Bookkeeping and 'Business Details' in addition to 'General Intelligence' lessons.

One of the study rooms in the 1930s.

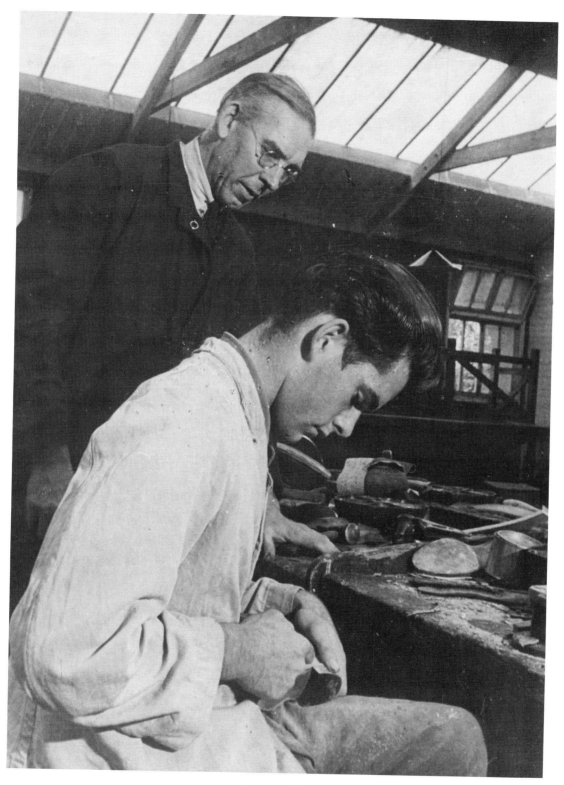

Boot making.

The students enjoyed two weeks holiday a year at Sandy Point, Hayling Island from the date it opened in 1919; but from 1927 to 1939 the boys, instead of going to Sandy Point, were sent to a camp arranged by the London House of Youth at Hawkeshill, Walmer, Kent. This proved most successful and gave the College students the opportunity of mixing with their peer group. In their first year they actually won a trophy for good behaviour and smartness.

It was always Treloar's intention that girls, too, should be included in the College but this was not to happen until 1965.

In the 1930s the pupils in the leatherwork shop made a lovely crocodile brief-case as well as a beautifully strong case with trays in which Mr. Langston (Consultant Orthopaedic Surgeon) used to carry his own personal operating equipment — and which he still has. They also made and sent (or took) Royal wedding presents as follows:-

(a)   H.R.H. Princess Mary - dressing case
(b)   H.R.H. The Duchess of York (now The Queen Mother) — suit case
(c)   H.R.H. The Duke of Kent — suit case taken to St. James' Palace
(d)   H.R.H. Duke of Gloucester — "a gift" and who, in return, sent a large enough portion of his wedding cake to be shared amongst the students.

One College boy had a stand in both the "Daily Mail" Exhibition at Olympia for ladies' handbags and also at the Boot Trade Fair at Islington.

The College inaugurated their own Magazine which the students composed, typed and duplicated themselves.

In 1934 there was great excitement as Sir Alan Cobham visited the Hospital by 'plane and kindly gave two boys a joy-ride.

During the Second World War, owing to the shortage of materials, leather work had to be given up and the course was replaced by a course in Radio and Television Servicing which proved very popular.

Thus it can readily be seen that the College fulfilled a great need and that the pupils were educated and turned out as useful members of society able to earn their own living; there are many letters of gratitude to testify to this.

The College continued on site for 45 years. After the National Health Service took over the Hospital in 1948 a decision was made that the College would remain independent and Trust funds were divided . . . but please read the following account written by the appeals Director of Lord Mayor Treloar Trust which brings the story up-to-date.

When the Lord Mayor Treloar Orthopaedic Hospital became a part of the National Health Service, the Trustees retained responsibility for the College and began the search for a new home so that it could move from the grounds of the Hospital. In any case, as far back as 1936, the Trustees had agreed that the College could not continue indefinitely to operate in

Lower School, Froyle (Photograph: Richard Hall).

a collection of old wooden huts.

It might be said that they went from one extreme to the other, for in 1949 the Trustees purchased beautiful Froyle Place, with its attractive gardens and park.

Froyle Place is an Elizabethan house, which was extensively altered in 1816. It dominates the small village of Upper Froyle, which stands on the north side of the Wey Valley about three miles from Alton and about five from Farnham, in a setting of rich farms and wooded downland. These farms, woods and downland were acquired by the Trustees in 1952, when they purchased the whole Froyle estate. This proved to be an astute investment when the greater part of the estate was sold in 1960 to finance the building of the Florence Treloar School for disabled girls.

The College's last term in the old wooden buildings ended on 1st April 1953. A week later the move began and was rapidly and successfully completed with the help of a party of masters and boys from Marlborough College who worked like fury for a week. They were so useful and enjoyed themselves so much that similar parties came from Marlborough to work on the estate every successive Easter holiday until the estate was sold in 1960.

The College staff from Alton also moved up to Froyle and were reinforced by the Bursar, his chief clerk, who had left the Hospital's finance department to work for the College, and the first Matron, who had for some years been coping with college boys as the sister in charge of Ward 5.

Shortly before the move, Miss Florence Treloar made her last public appearance as a Trustee when she planted two trees in the courtyard of the new College. Upon her death she left to the College all Sir William Treloar's orders and decorations as well as many other relics of the honours he had received during his life of public service.

At this time — 1953 — Stanley Evans, Consultant Orthopaedic Surgeon at Treloar Hospital, joined the Board of the Treloar College Trustees and eventually became their chairman. For although an independent body, the College and its activities were of deep importance to the Hospital.

The first term at Froyle began on 27th April 1953 with 44 boys — which quite by chance worked out at one for each full year of the College's previous existence.

The College was still providing three-year training courses, with part-time education, for boys between the ages of 14 and 20 years. In 1953 there were four courses — radio service work (later radio and TV servicing); surgical shoe making; tailoring and gardening. A fifth course in pig and poultry keeping was started in 1954 but, owing to lack of applicants, ceased in 1968. By 1954 the College roll had increased to 61 and it remained full until a major development in its work two years later.

Compared with the College's previous "home" the new buildings were so spacious and splendid that many of the boys at first viewed them with feelings almost of awe. It was an amazing transformation. In the next term or two the College happily settled down to its new life.

Meanwhile, the Trustees were considering how the potentialities of Froyle Place could most usefully be developed. After discussion in which the special services branch of the then Ministry of Education and a number of Education Authorities were involved, it became clear that there was a real need for a boarding school for physically handicapped boys offering academic education such as a grammar school would provide. In addition, full time education for boys below grammar school standard should also be provided and the existing training courses maintained.

So in 1954 Mr. Christopher Green was commissioned to design new buildings to house another 70 boys and additional staff, and to accommodate full-time educational courses as well as a sixth training course. Also to be planned were a gymnasium, an indoor swimming pool and a sick bay.

These new buildings were finished by the late summer of 1956 and in September of that year the organisation of the College was radically changed. The age of admission was lowered to 11 years; all boys had to undertake a full-time education course until they reached the age of 16 at least; and the training courses, still of three years duration, were to be open only to boys over 16 years.

The College cricket team in the 1930s.

There were now 105 boys in the College. Over the next five terms the total increased to just over the official maximum of 130; with boys coming from all over the British Isles and even a few from overseas.

The new buildings were officially opened on 26th June 1957 by Viscount Hailsham (then Minister of Education) in the presence of many friends and supporters of the Trustees. The additional accommodation and the greatly increased staff made possible numerous fresh activities in and out of school hours. A variety of clubs and societies, catering for a wide range of interests, came into being. The College was run as nearly as possible as an ordinary boarding school, and offered as full and varied a life as might be found in any other of equivalent size with facilities far superior to those in most.

This was almost a fairy story development to Sir William Treloar's original dreams of helping crippled children to escape from the dark poverty of Victorian and Edwardian slums.

Through the College a large number of boys had been enabled to embark upon successful careers and thus become independent after leaving. Life in the College had enabled them to learn how much they could do; it had encouraged, and even compelled, them to do it; and in the process had invariably given them the physical and moral confidence without which they could hardly take their place in the life and work of the country on equal terms with those who were not so disabled.

This has been the College's aim since it was founded. There was just one important link missing. It had always been in the minds of the Founder and Trustees that eventually similar education should be provided for girls. In 1960, the Trustees decided the time had arrived for them to embark on the provision of a boarding school for physically handicapped girls.

The five Trustees, all busy men and, with one exception, not otherwise concerned with schools, decided that they needed advice on the education of girls. Accordingly, after appropriate negotiations, an instrument of government was issued by the Ministry of Education, and under its terms

The Upper School, Holybourne – 1988 (Photograph: Richard Hall).

118

a number of Governors were appointed to assist the Trustees. Since 1960, Trustees and Governors together have formed the governing body of the College — and later of the new Florence Treloar School, to which the first girls came in September 1965.

Before embarking on the building of the girls' school, the Trustees ascertained that the project would have the backing of the Ministry of Education and local education authorities.

The money to build the school was found by the Trust through selling the greater part of the Froyle Estate, which had been bought with Froyle Place in 1949. The Estate also included a plot of land at Holybourne which the Trustees retained and on which the school was built.

The foundation stone was laid on 17th May 1963 by Colonel C. Newton-Davis, who had been a Trustee since 1950 and became chairman in 1963 upon Lord Burnham's death. Not only was he extremely active in the establishment and development of the College at Froyle, but he bore the burden fully of the foundation of the girls' school. He saw the school open in 1965 but unfortunately died before the official opening.

This took place on 2nd May 1967, when Princess Alexandra, following the great interest shown by her late father, the Duke of Kent, honoured the Trust by lunching with the governing body at the Lord Mayor Treloar College. Then, in the afternoon, in the presence of some 700 guests, she formally opened the Florence Treloar School by unveiling a portrait of Miss Florence Treloar.

In the beginning the school had 40 pupils and this quickly rose to 90. The girls were encouraged to be independent and to meet other children socially and competitively. The School endeavoured to teach them to cope with adult life and to do this the young disabled needed to be educated to overcome their handicaps without looking to others for help. At the weekend, they were allowed into Alton and further afield if they could cope with the train or a Ministry of Health tricycle.

The School offered a wide range of sporting activities and facilities for physical education, gymnastics, badminton and archery. For example, a team from the School competed in the National Junior Stoke Mandeville Games. Indeed the girls won the trophy two years running. Resulting from this the 1970's senior girl was selected for the British Team in the Commonwealth Paraplegic Games in New Zealand, where she and a former pupil won seven medals between them

In 1978, the boys' College at Froyle and the Florence Treloar School for girls were amalgamated to provide a co-educational establishment with the Upper School at Holybourne and the Lower School at Froyle and together called the Lord Mayor Treloar College. The College is recognised by the Department of Education and Science as a non-maintained special boarding school which provides primary and secondary school education for physically

119

handicapped boys and girls aged 8 to 16 years, and further education for similar students aged 16-19 plus. They come from all over the country and suffer from almost every form of physical disablement — particularly Spina Bifida, Cerebral Palsy, Muscular Dystrophy, Haemophelia, fragile bones, heart conditions, epilepsy, chronic juvenile arthritis and handicaps resulting from serious traffic and sporting accidents.

The College specialises in catering for the above average ability student and offers more than 20 examination subjects at GCSE. Average and below-average pupils with moderate learning difficulties have tailor-made Courses to suit their needs in small classes with specialist support teaching when required.

On 30 October 1984 Her Royal Highness the Duchess of Gloucester formally opened Gloucester House — the College's new Sixth Form Building.

The separate extension enables the students to have more freedom to mix with able bodied youngsters, to live independently for trial periods in flats and to learn how to look after themselves in different situations. In this upper age group, the need is even more pressing since local authorities rarely have special schools for the disabled which can provide suitable courses for the over 16 group or anything similar to the 'Education for Life' course, a concept initiated at Holybourne in the early 1980's to cover every aspect of the transition from sheltered existence at a school to independent life in the open community. The College took an early lead in the development of this work, which was greeted with enthusiasm by students, educational workers and Social Services alike.

Between the wars, and in the early post-war years, the emphasis had been on training pupils in practical skills; over the more recent past the trend has moved towards giving them as complete an education as possible stretching their minds to the full.

New medical techniques and improved surgical skills have enabled many more handicapped children to survive into adulthood. This trend, coupled with the National drive to integrate as many handicapped pupils as possible in normal schools, has meant that the College has of necessity accepted pupils with even more severe handicaps than hitherto. At the same time, increasing unemployment has made the prospect of finding jobs for the disabled even more daunting. It became apparent therefore that the aim should be redefined so as to include the need to develop the potential of each pupil in whatever way would enable him or her to live his life to the full, either by way of full or part-time employment, or by the development of a satisfying and possibly rewarding hobby or interest — subject only to the unavoidable effect of his or her handicap.

As part of their drive towards meeting this need, the Trustees were able to finance a new Craft Room, which was opened in 1982, during which year Sir Alan Traill visited the College as an Alderman and Sheriff. As

College students in their version of 'H.M.S. Pinafore' (1985).

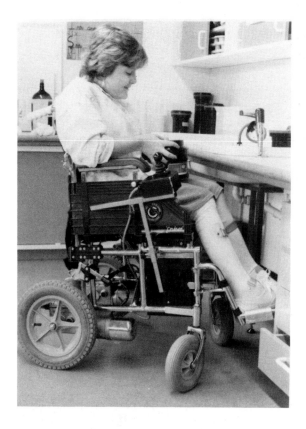

Student Karen Ashworth attending a photography lesson – 1988 (Photograph: Richard Hall).

a result of this visit he offered, during his year as Lord Mayor of London, to raise money for a significant expansion of the College facilities for training 6th Form pupils in vocational skills, and for improving the Therapy facilities at the Upper School. Another major appeal was therefore launched by Sir Alan at the Mansion House in November 1984. Two years later, nearly a million pounds was raised and the Traill Centre was built. It was taken into use in September 1986 and opened by HRH The Prince of Wales in March 1987. The Centre contains an extensive Business Studies area, an area devoted to Textile Work, and two Light Industrial areas; there are also facilities for the assessment of individual abilities, as well as a Computer Room, Music Recording Room and Photographic Dark Room. Other facilities can be added as necessary, for the Centre is designed on modern 'open plan' lines, so that the College can respond to the different needs of a succession of pupils, to the extent, if necessary, of providing tailor-made courses for individual students.

The new Therapy Centre, which replaces unacceptably cramped and scattered accommodation, combines Occupational, Physio and Speech

Modern study at the College (1988).
Above: 5th Form biology lesson – from left to right: Karl Chuter, Ashraf Atalla,
Martin Lazell (teacher), Suzanne Paull, Angela Brinsden, Louise Kennedy.
Below: Ian Kenny concentrating on computer programming.

Therapy in one area, and incorporates a Bio-Engineering workshop.

Although such an approach to 6th Form work is costly, the Governors are convinced that it is essential if each individual is to develop all his or her potential abilities as fully as possible: it is, also, the logical development of the ideas of the Founder, modified by the changing circumstances of today.

In 1985 the Trust created a new post of Occupational Liaison Officer whose prime task would be to research ways in which young people who have left the College recently are coping with life and what occupations they are following. The findings should be invaluable in modifications to the curriculum for present pupils and in advising them about their future. The appointment is known as the Billesden Officer, as the official's salary is paid from a fund generously set up for the College by the Skinners' and Merchant Taylors' Companies.

Over the past 80 years the activities of the College have expanded dramatically. For example, driving lessons are in popular demand and the College now has its own car, adapted for handicapped students. The enthusiasm of the horticultural students can be judged by their successes in the City and Guild examinations and in selling their plants at the annual Garden Open Day in May.

Drama and Music flourish. The College sports teams have a considerable reputation at regional and national level. With more than three-quarters of the pupils in wheel-chairs, most sports have to be adapted, and in the Games run by the British Association for the Disabled there are frequent wins at athletics, table-tennis, bowls, swimming, archery, basket-ball, shooting and snooker.

Mr. Richard Browne, Orthopaedic Consultant at Basingstoke District Hospital and Treloars, visits the College regularly to advise on care of the children there and when they have problems many of them visit Treloar's out-patients for advice, or are admitted to the Children's Ward for treatment, so the link with the Hospital is maintained although to a lesser degree.

The Treloar Haemophilia Centre

In 1956 the first haemophiliacs were admitted to the College. Treatment with plasma — a long and tedious affair taking up to two hours — was available, on request, at the Hospital and a local General Practitioner undertook the care of the boys at the College.

Dr. S.G. Rainsford was appointed as a Research Fellow in 1968 and the treatment of haemophiliacs entered the modern era. He established a research laboratory at the Hospital and in 1972 the Treloar Haemophilia

1952 – Members of the Hospital staff with over 30 years' service.
Standing (left to right): Mr. Thorley (Supplies Officer), Mr. Ware (i/c Surgical Appliance Shop), Mr. Mylward (Chauffeur Mechanic), Mr. Smith (retired October, 1952), Mr. Skates (Garden staff), Mr. Thurston (Garden staff).
Front row (l. to r.): Mr. Walker (Surgical Appliance Shop), Mr. Brown (Clinical Records Office), Mr. Drake (Head Porter). Photograph: Rob Small.

Centre was officially established under the Directorship of Dr. P.G. Arblaster. By now commercially produced Factor VIII was available which provided the haemophiliac with an opportunity for a more independent life-style. A teaching programme was set up aiming to teach every haemophiliac the techniques of preparation and self-administration. Factor VIII was stored at home so that they could transfuse themselves when a bleed occurred which meant that for the first time a haemophiliac was more independent with far fewer days off school or work.

Dr. A. Aronstam took over the Directorship in 1977 and the following year all facilities were transferred to the Lord Mayor Treloar College at Holybourne where this National Health Service Unit is physically attached to the College Medical Centre.

A Consultant Orthopaedic Surgeon, Mr. Richard Browne, sees cases at a joint clinic regularly.

Seventh Royal Visit

In 1956 Princess Alexandra of Kent visited the Hospital and presented Certificates and Awards to the nurses.

A group of uniformed nurses formed a guard of honour as she alighted from her car at the entrance to Beech House. She wore a red hat and coat. She was welcomed by Lord Burnham, Miss Walker, Mr. Evans, Mr. Cane and flowers were presented to her by Student Nurse Asbury.

PART IV

1968-1988

Development 1968-1988

With the partial closure of the Alton General Hospital and the transfer of the medical and surgical units to four vacated wards at the Lord Mayor Treloar Hospital, the latter became a busy general hospital complex with emergency services including a casualty department. At the same time, the Regional Board began to appoint additional consultants for the new Basingstoke Hospital project, to work at the Lord Mayor Treloar Hospital and build up local hospital services. This intrusion into Treloar Hospital pressured, but equally stimulated, the orthopaedic services.

Stanley Evans was the senior surgeon at that time with Stanley Cane, his faithful Hospital Secretary, an act often referred to as 'the two Stanleys'. The work of the Hospital was still orientated towards children but many adults suffering from skeletal tuberculosis and poliomyelitic paralysis were also referred from the Region. In addition, there were large numbers of children with club feet, congenital dislocations and Perthe's Disease of the hips in addition to scoliosis, occupying 80 beds distributed into four wards. There was one female adult ward which was full of patients with osteoarthritic hips at various stages of recovery following femoral osteotomies, as this was the treatment of choice in those days because joint replacement was still in its infancy. So there were many adult patients and children occupying the 200 orthopaedic beds, but their management was frequently non-operative or conservative in nature. Colleagues at this time included Peter Arblaster (Consultant Physician), James Moseley (Consultant Surgeon) Francis Moynihan (Consultant Orthopaedic Surgeon) and "Harry" Haysom (Consultant Surgeon).

The retirement of Stanley Evans and his colleagues, Dennis Wilson and Heber Langston, heralded a new era in the orthopaedic services. At the same time, the appointment of Dr. McIntosh and Dr. Judith Darmady as paediatricians brought in a new urgency to the children's service and the introduction of new surgical techniques speeded up the occupancy of beds. On the adult side, osteotomies gave way to joint replacements, which meant shorter post-operative convalescence, making room for more patients to be admitted. Thus, the operating theatres were hard pushed to deal with this new wave of orthopaedic surgery, as well as the general surgical services.

In 1969, Dr. John Revans, the Senior Medical Officer of the Wessex Regional Hospital Board became so concerned by the increase in waiting lists for orthopaedic surgery in the Wessex Region, that he asked for a conference and working report on a proposed regional orthopaedic service. Eventually, monies were made available for the upgrading of the operating theatres, including the construction of a 'temporary' Octatent theatre, which was built in the main hall of the hospital, to cope with the extra work. Surgeons from Portsmouth and Winchester were invited to work at Treloar Hospital with the Alton and Southampton consultants and a thriving Regional Orthopaedic Service developed over the next ten years.

Cemented components in hip and knee replacements were introduced in 1970, and two operating theatres were totally dedicated and reserved for orthopaedic surgery; subsequently the number of patients admitted for joint replacement increased each year until in 1987, 750 were treated. The gradual withdrawal of general medicine and surgery into the new Basingstoke Hospital gave further space for reorganisation. The closure of Colin Jardine's two wards provided new space for the development of the physiotherapy department. The hydrotherapy pool was upgraded to cope mainly with the increased number of children and adults in postoperative recovery from hip surgery.

In 1970, the Ministry of Health requested the British Orthopaedic Association to establish training centres for young surgeons throughout the country, and Southampton was chosen as one such centre. Four senior registrar posts were appointed to rotate between Portsmouth, Southampton and Treloar Hospital. In 1973, monies were raised by the Regional Board to build and equip a Regional Orthopaedic library, and more than a thousand pounds was donated by the John Wade Trust to equip this new branch of the Wessex Regional Library and Information Service. It was opened by Professor Shackleton in 1973 and named the Sir Henry Gauvain Library. Mrs. Janice Mayhew was appointed as the Librarian and subsequently she has been responsible for its development and later transfer to Beech House, in December 1986. It has now become one of the most modern orthopaedic libraries in the country, providing a personal service to all the regional orthopaedic surgeons and also to all health care staff in the Treloar Chase Unit and Treloar College. It uses a computer system not only for research facilities, but also to maintain its loan records; approximately 300 books are added each year and it has over 100 current journals.

A modern elective orthopaedic hospital is dependent upon the dedication of its medical, nursing and ancillary staff. The success of the Treloar story is due to such devotion of service. The build up of consultant staff during the 1970s and the improved standard of work attracted not only young orthopaedic surgeons for training, but also skilled orthopaedic nurses; their training school established itself as one of the most successful orthopaedic

The Hospital staff in the 1970s.

1973 – Professor Robert Salter, of the Toronto Hospital for Sick Children and Sims Commonwealth Professor, signing the visitors' book at Alton. Behind him are Mr. Macrae, Professor J. Ellis and Mr. John Wilkinson (Photograph: Rob Small, Alton).

1975 – Henry Cooper, the popular British boxer, came to the Hospital after opening the Sports Centre at Alton.

training schools in the country and its examination success rate is second to none.

The Plaster Theatre carries on the tradition of Gauvain in making a major contribution to orthopaedic care. This was run for many years by Sister Phyll Bryant and upon her retirement was taken over by Sister Prior.

Property belonging to the Hospital was sold off and this included:-
Wykeham House, King's Road, Alton — an extension of the Nurses' Home; Westbank, Basingstoke Road, Alton — which housed the physiotherapists; Alderney House, Normandy Street, Alton — married families accommodation and Ashdell Cottage, Ashdell Road, Alton — also married families accommodation.

Save Treloar Campaign

For many years the fate of the Hospital was in jeopardy. The Wessex Regional Health Authority planned to transfer the elective orthopaedic services of the Hospital to District Hospitals by about 1981, thus hoping to provide comprehensive orthopaedic cover in Basingstoke, Winchester, Southampton and Portsmouth. However the move was opposed by the Consultants, staff, patients and local people on the grounds that if the Hospital were to close, its qualities would never be re-established elsewhere — the expertise would simply be diminished and disappear in a very short time.

Five action groups, organised by Sister Prior, were formed within the Hospital with the object of bringing pressure to bear upon the Regional Health Authority and the D.H.S.S. to keep the Hospital open. Action consisted of:-

(a) a petition signed by former and present patients and staff of the Hospital which was sent to the Regional Health Authority.

(b) two Public Debates held at the Assembly Rooms, Alton — that on 15th February 1978, chaired by Mr. Michael Mates (then MP for the area) broke up in total confusion.

(c) requests to ex-patients encouraging them to write to the Regional Health Authority, their MP, the Rt. Hon. David Ennals MP, Secretary of State for Social Services, and Dr. Gerard Vaughan, Shadow Minister of Health. Some 550 letters were sent to each.

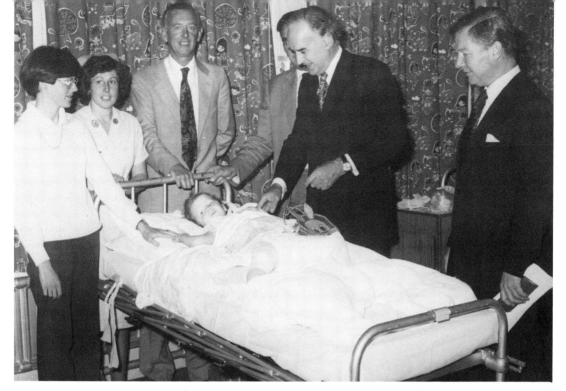

1978 – First visit of Dr. Gerard Vaughan, M.P. to the Hospital, when he was Shadow Minister of Health.
Left to right: Mrs. Linda Flood (mother of the young patient) S.E.N. Jean Costello, Mr. Francis Moynihan, FRCS, Mr. Michael Mates, M.P., Dr. Vaughan, Mr. John Wilkinson, FRCS (Photograph: Kimroy Photography, Alton).

(d) a deputation to the House of Commons with the object of lobbying Hampshire MPs.
(e) provision of stickers for cars and posters.
(f) successfully arousing interest of the British Orthopaedic Association.
(g) arranging two visits to the Hospital by Dr. Gerard Vaughan who took up the case (successfully).
(h) arranging publicity in the media — local and national press, Radio Solent, BBC 'Jimmy Young Programme' Southern Television etc.
(j) staff and friends numbering 400 marched with banners from the Hospital through the streets of Alton and back again. Patients came out on the verandah to cheer the protesters. This was given television coverage.

As surgeons, in Basingstoke District Hospital, prepared to operate on an Alton patient they lifted his smock and found a "Save Treloar" sticker on his stomach!

On 28th September, 1978 Dr. Gerard Vaughan, Shadow Minister of Health, visited the Hospital and said that he did not think that the administrators had looked at the situation carefully enough and he was not sure that their assurances that orthopaedic standards could be met outside a specialist centre were correct. He agreed to take up the matter with Mr. David Ennals, the Minister of Health, and promised that should the Conservatives get into power in the General Election in 1979, he, Vaughan, promised to see that the Hospital would remain open. They did and he did.

Finally, in November, 1980, Dr. Gerard Vaughan (now Minister of Health) paid a second visit to the Hospital and subsequently wrote a letter ensuring the future of the Hospital. Staff, patients, friends and inhabitants of Alton were jubilant. Investment and up-dating started at once and is still continuing with the Hospital looking ever forward with orthopaedics.

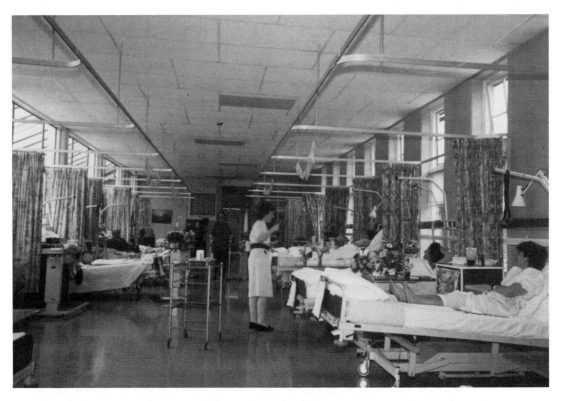

The modern Ward Eight.

Success – November, 1980 (left to right): Paul Bayliss, John Wilkinson, Mrs. Lynda Chalker, M.P., Miss V. Billin, Dr. Gerard Vaughan, M.P. (Minister of Health) and Lord Northbrook.

Hospital Chapel

The responsibility for the Chapel was initially undertaken by All Saints, Alton which, in those days, always had a curate. Sundays started with Holy Communion at 6 or 6.30 a.m. for staff before they went on duty; it was followed by a simple service for the children which was more or less compulsory for those who were ambulant or able to be pushed to the Chapel in their chairs or trolleys. Evening Song (or Complins) for resident staff who were off duty and for those who could be spared from the wards completed Sunday worship. The degree of compulsion for the two latter services was dependent on the views of each ward sister or Matron.

In addition, Holy Communion was, of course, taken round the wards regularly and during the week each ward had its own service in the late afternoon after school had finished. When the Hospital became part of the N.H.S. it continued to be served by local parishes (which now included Selborne) and by Father Peter from Beech Abbey. The pattern of formal worship changed as the churches lost their curates. Services became more ward orientated and ecumenical.

Apart from the element of compulsion, the principle remains of pastoral care of all patients and staff whatever their denomination.

Children's Wards

Children admitted are suffering from polio, cerebral palsy, spina bifida, scoliosis, but by far the greatest proportion is congenital dislocation of the hip. In 1984 a support group, called H.I.P.S., (Help in Plaster and Splints) was formed in order to buy special equipment such as car seats, buggeys and C.D.H. chairs to help children in plaster. They also made a video film of children in various stages of treatment and give advice as to how best to help them. Their preparation for an operation has already been touched upon under 'Hospital School'. The children are taught of theatre procedures through play. Theatre staff visit the children (prior to surgery) dressed in their theatre gowns and masks. Patterned gowns are used instead of the usual white so that they appear less clinical and more interesting. Children are taken to theatre in their beds instead of being transferred to a trolley in order to save disturbing them.

After surgery they are presented with a 'Treloar Ted' Certificate to thank them for attending theatre and being good. Theatre staff, ward staff, ward therapist, teachers and parents all work closely together in the preparation of the child for surgery, the aim being to make the child's stay in hospital pleasant and as short as possible.

1983 – Celebrating the Hospital's 75th Anniversary.
Above (left to right): Mr. John Wilkinson, Mr. J. Cholmeley, Mr. E. Smythe,
Dr. R. Murray, Mr. H. H. Langston, Prof. J. Ellis.
Below: Sister Phyll Bryant with Fr. Peter, from Beech Abbey.

Physiotherapy Department

by Geraldine Walker

The Society of Trained Masseuses was founded in 1895 by 10 Nurses who were then practising medical rubbing and remedial gymnastics; thus the physiotherapy undertaken in 1908 was by Sisters trained in these skills.

It is a mark of the 'Happy Hospital' that only three Heads of Physiotherapy have been appointed since its inception, Sister Alice Smith, Miss Evelyn Newing and Miss Geraldine Walker.

In the early days, as previously explained, treatment was mainly for tuberculous joints and spine. By 1933 the Hospital had become a centre of excellence in the treatment of patients suffering from Lupus and Cerebral Palsy and several qualified masseuses worked at the Hospital, unpaid (apart from board and lodging) for a period of three months to gain experience in the treatment of these conditions.

The 18 outlying clinics run by the Hospital were visited by masseuses on a regular basis once or twice a week. Splints were provided, advice given on exercises and the patients monitored. The masseuses worked closely with the splint makers at the Hospital who made (or repaired) all the splints as necessary.

In the early 1940s and again in the 1950s there were two poliomyelitis epidemics from which many patients were treated, following the acute stage, by rehabilitation and surgery. All polio patients were treated in the hydrotherapy pool (the second one in the country) and this, of course, caused an enormous increase in the workload. Patients were also taken swimming — first to the Military Baths at Aldershot two evenings a week in a Warren's removal van and later to the College swimming pool at Froyle.

A service was provided at the isolation hospitals at Aldershot and St. Paul's, Winchester for polio victims who needed daily stretching and passive movements. Some patients were on respirators and needed chest physiotherapy. The majority of these patients were later transferred to the Hospital for surgery and rehabilitation. Home visits and wheelchair assessments were done with the physiotherapists working closely with the occupational therapists. Operations were done most days. These were great times with enthusiastic patients and staff who worked on together long after they should have stopped. They were also involved in the social events at the Hospital such as swimming galas, matches and other entertainments.

At the Hospital virtually all the patients treated were in-patients. Some of the staff went to Wigan to observe the surgery and follow-up treatment for the early hip replacements performed by Mr. Charnley.

Dr. J.B. Morrison was appointed as Consultant in Physical Medicine (later Rheumatology and Rehabilitation) in 1961.

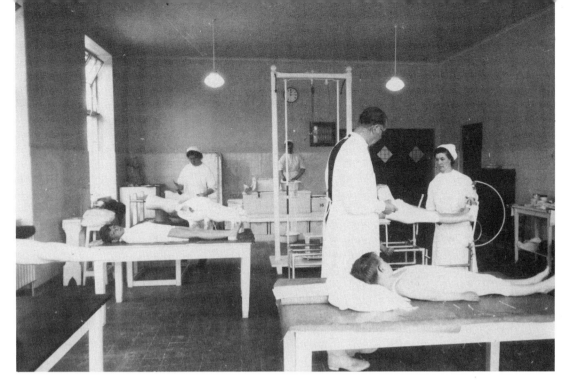

Above: Dr. C. E. M. Jones in the Physiotherapy Department – 1940. Below: the department in 1965.

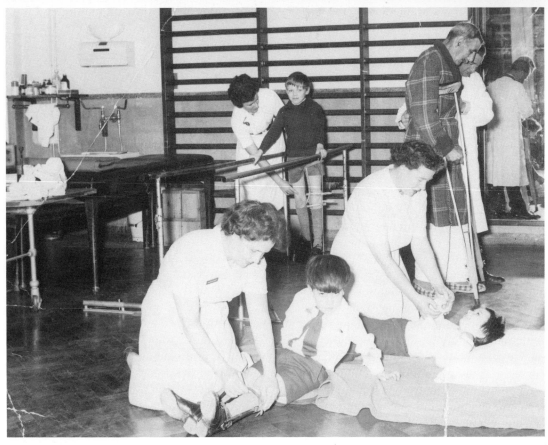

The Physiotheraphy Department, 1965.

Miss Geraldine Walker took over as Superintendent in 1967 following which many changes have taken place.

All non-orthopaedic cases were transferred to the new Basingstoke District Hospital in the 1970s and there was an expansion in the adult orthopaedic cases. There was also a steady increase in the demand for out-patient treatment.

In the late 1970s the Elderly Care Service at Alton General Hospital was extended and with the opening of Inwood Ward there was a much greater physiotherapy input into Alton General Hospital. A small Day Unit was opened there which was extended in 1987. The 'Mary Rose' Elderly Care Unit is staffed by a part-time physiotherapist and an assistant.

In 1981 a pilot scheme for Open Access for the General Practitioners was started and this service was extended to all the GPs in Alton, Four Marks, Ropley and Bentley. This scheme is for acute conditions only and now accounts for 60% of the out-patients' workload. Nearly 50% of the out-patients have neck or back problems so most of the staff have mobilising expertise.

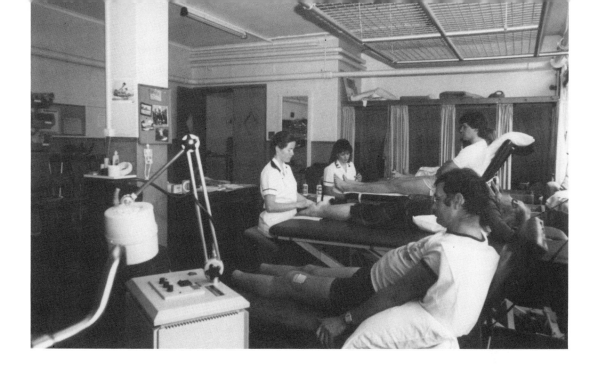

The Hospital to-day – Two views of the Physiotherapy Department.

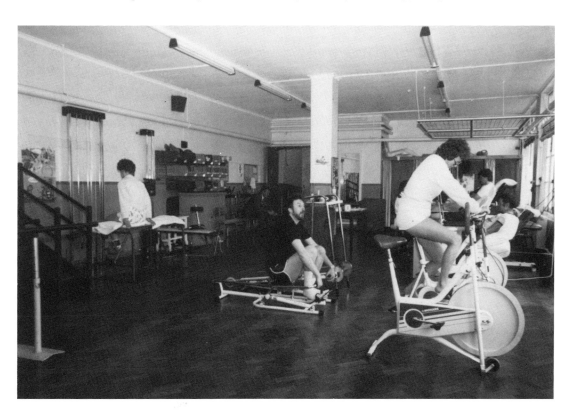

In 1985 the Elizabeth Dibben Clinic in Bordon was opened and the Physiotherapy Department provides Open Access service for the GPs in that area three mornings a week. The following year the Hospital also took over the management of Odiham Cottage Hospital and a daily physiotherapy service was commenced there for the in-patients and a few GP Open Access patients.

A 'Back School' is run on a regular basis and when staffing permits, and the demand is there, 'keep fit' classes are held for the Hospital staff.

The Mary Rose Elderly Care Unit

In 1982 the Portsmouth Block was adapted for the long term care of elderly patients. The original patients came from Winchfield Hospital which was closed as part of Basingstoke and North Hants Health Authority's rationalisation of services.

In 1985, the Unit was linked with the facilities at Alton General Hospital.

An attempt is made to create a happy and relaxed environment for the elderly patients on both hospital sites in Alton.

The Treloar patients decided to rename their wards 'Mary Rose' continuing the links with Portsmouth and commemorating the name of the first sister in charge of the ward who had transferred from Winchfield with her patients, Sister Mary Powell. Individual care, physiotherapy and occupational therapy are available to all patients who are very much in charge of their own lives. They are able to receive visitors at any time, to go out on family trips or to go in small groups to the theatre, the local pub., Wisley Gardens, Birdworld, shopping or any other activities which appeal. Entertainments are arranged on the ward and evening events such as Beetle Drives, Concerts etc. involve the whole family, including grandchildren. Patients are able to garden, birdwatch and get into the fresh air whenever the weather is suitable. Pets are a feature of ward life including budgerigars, goldfish, 'Fergie' the cat and visits from 'Pat a Dog' and their own family dogs are encouraged.

Visitors are welcome at any time, a hairdressing service is available and breakfast in bed is an option; flexible waking and retiring times are also encouraged.

The object of the Elderly Care Unit is to provide individual care and rehabilitation facilities for the local elderly.

A point worth making is that some nurses at the Hospital in the 1920s and 1930s are now being cared for in the Unit.

Theatre

In 1975 the total number of orthopaedic cases operated upon was 1,781; this had risen in 1987 to 2,221 — an increase of 440.

There was a similarly large increase in joint replacements, i.e. the total number of joint replacements undertaken in 1975 was 458 but in 1987 this had risen to 763.

The figures speak for themselves.

Closing Comments by Mr. Paul Bayliss, General Manager

Following the long period of uncertainty about the Hospital's future during the 1970s and the Minister of Health's decision in 1980 to save the Hospital, the Basingstoke and North Hants Health Authority invested a considerable amount of money in the Hospital which helped underpin its future as an Orthopaedic Centre. Approximately two million pounds has been spent over the last ten years in upgrading wards, replacement of equipment throughout the Hospital, converting the former Burnham Ward to a modern Out-Patient Department, opening the Gauvain Wing (Private Orthopaedic Unit) and providing accommodation for the elderly ('Mary Rose' ward).

The Regional and District Health Authorities have approved further plans and investment which will provide two new theatres and an extension to the Hospital for elderly patients.

The Hospital has seen considerable change over the last eighty years and it will go on to meet the continually changing requirements but, as through all its history, it will provide a special service in a centre of excellence.

Conclusion

There is a spirit in both Hospital and College which is difficult to define but it is there. It is certain that Treloar would have approved of the work currently being undertaken — the advanced surgery at the Hospital and the training of the severely disabled at the College — both establishments are internationally renowned — what a fitting memorial!

Retirement of Stanley Maxim, deputy head porter.
Back row (in white jackets): Dick Lowton (Post Porter), Christopher Edwards, Stephen Boucher (Physio Porter), Stephen Abbott, David Lawry, David Andrews (Theatre Porter) and Michael Atkins.
Middle Row: Alf Goddard (Head Porter – and on the staff for 40 years), Gary Trickey, Christopher Reeves (Night Porter) and Bert Pike.
Front row (retired staff): Albert Clarke (Theatre), Fred Rogers, Jack Palmer, Stanley and Kathleen Maxim (Mrs. Maxim was formerley on the staff), Arthur Rolfe and Mick Scott.

Bibliographical Notes

The most important single source for this book was the Annual Reports contained in the Hospital Library (actual references are held by the Librarian). In addition correspondence with, and reminiscences of, close personal friends have provided a good deal of information.

Books used were:-
'A Lord Mayor's Diary' by Treloar
'Sir William Purdie Treloar' by C. E. Lawrence.

Alphabetical List of Consultant Orthopaedic Surgeons

Mr. John Allison
Mr. K. de Belder
Mr. N. A. Boyd
Mr. Richard Browne
Mr. Nicholas Clarke
Mr. Robin Denham
Mr. E. Stanley Evans
Professor James S. Ellis
Sir H. A. Thomas Fairbank
Mr. Anthony Fitzgerald
Mr. Martin Grover
Professor E. W. Hey Groves
Mr. Kenneth T. Hesketh
Mr. Michael Hunter
Mr. Robert Jackson
Mr. Ian Jeffery
Mr. H. Heber Langston
Mr. E. A. Lindsay
Mr. D. E. Macrae
Mr. Francis J. Moynihan
Mr. Charles Murray
Mr. J. Robertson
Mr. A. Samuel
Professor John Shearer
Mr. E. H. J. Smythe
Mr. Neil Thomas
Mr. John A. Wilkinson
Mr. J. Dennis Wilson
Mr. Stephen Wood

List of Matrons

Robertson	1908 — 1935
Holborrow	1935 — 1946
Walker	1946 — 1960
McQueen	1960 — 1963/4
Peacock	1963/4 — 1968
Robertson	1968 — 1972
Billen	1972 — 1984

The Tree upon which the badge of the Orthopaedic Associations of the world is based

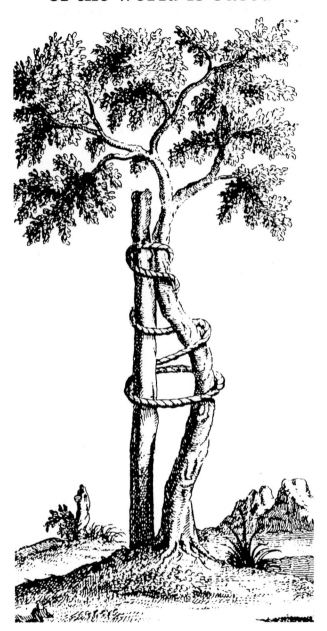

Excerpt from Nicolas Andry's book 'Orthopaedia' dated 1743.

"In a word the same method must be used in this case, for recovering the shape of the leg as is used for making straight the crooked trunk of a young tree."

ORTHOS = Greek for "straighten — correction of deformity"

PAIS = Greek for "a child"

Thus ORTHOPAEDIC

LORD MAYOR TRELOAR

CRIPPLES' HOSPITAL AND COLLEGE

ALTON 1908

1. Alton Park Station — Private Siding
2. Laundry
3. Power House
4. School Room for Ambulant Patients
5. New Isolation Hospital
6. College Recreation Hall, Dormitories, Dining Room etc.
7. College Workshops
8. Engineer's Quarters
9. Entrance
10. Museum
11. Garage
12. Hard Tennis Courts
13. Treatment Block containing X-Ray Dept., Dispensary, Operating Theatre, Massage and Plaster Rooms
14. A.1. Ward Florence Treloar Ward for Nurses
15. B.10. Ward School & Teachers' Preparation Room
16. Offices, Laboratory, etc.
17. B.3. Ward Light Department
18. Memorial Bust of Founder
19. Queen Alexandra Nurses' Home
20. Kitchens & Staff Dining Rooms etc.
21. Matron and Night Nurses' Quarters
22. Chapel
23. Assistant Resident Medical Officers' Quarters
24. Steward's Bungalow
25. Domestics' Quarters
26. Trustees' House
27. Medical Superintendent's Bungalow
28. Grass Tennis Courts
29. Surgical Shop — under Solarium between Wards
30. Light Department
31. Flat for Teacher
32. Lupus Girls
33. Ward for College boys and Flat for Male Nurse
34. Pets
35. Flat for Male Teacher
36. Lupus Boys
37. Teacher's Flat
38. Tree planted by Queen Alexandra
39. Tree planted by Queen Amelia
40. Pigsties
41. Water Tower
42. Water Tower

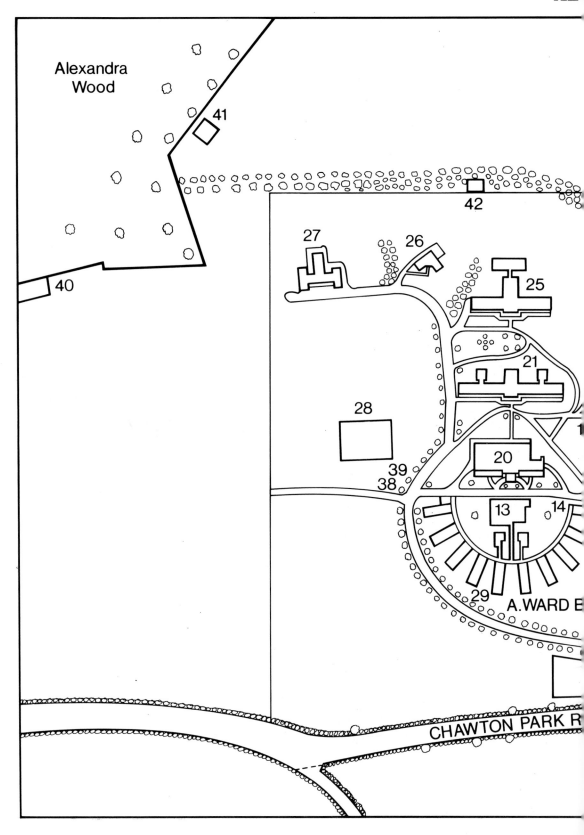

Alexandra
Wood

41

40

42

27

26

25

21

28

39
38

20

13   14

29   A. WARD E

CHAWTON PARK R

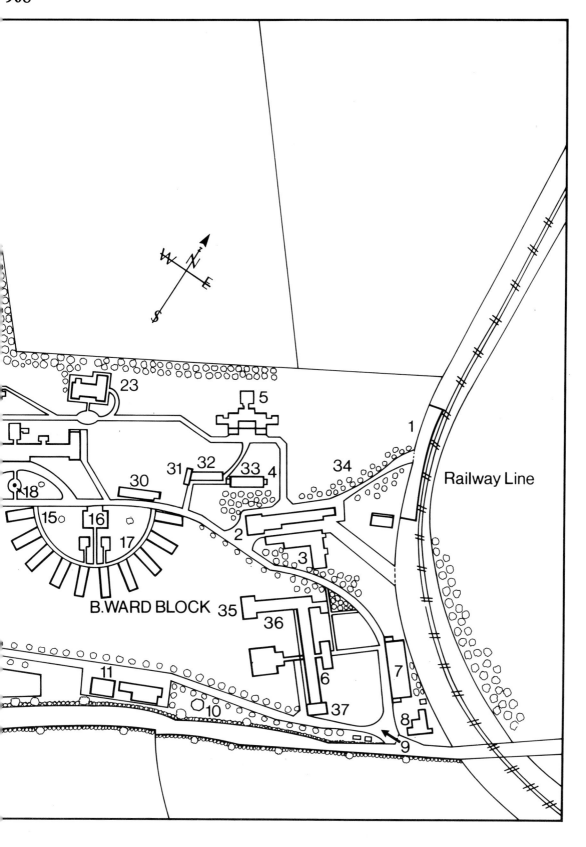

Railway Line

B. WARD BLOCK

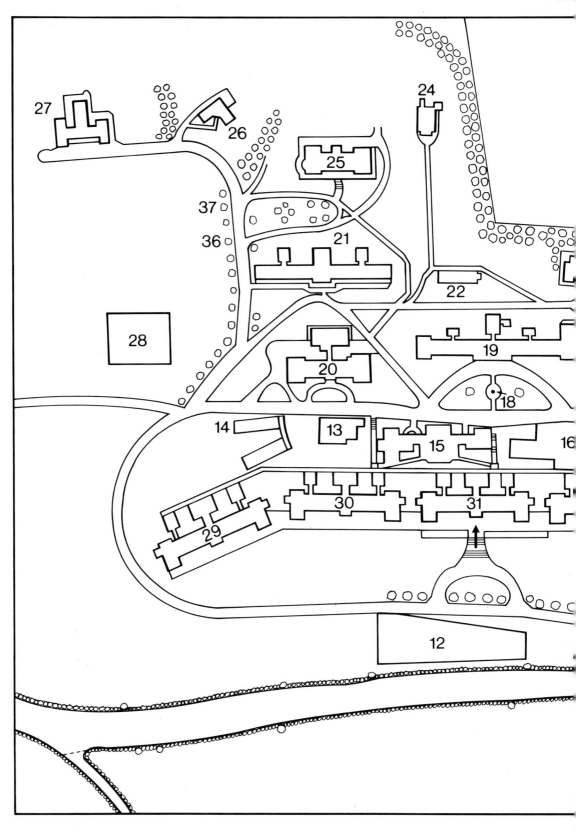

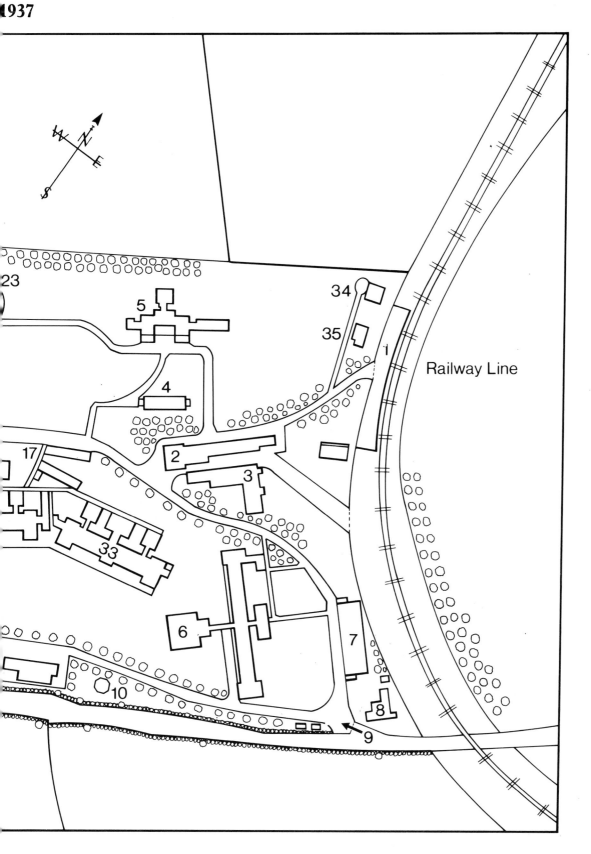

Railway Line

LORD MAYOR TRELOAR

CRIPPLES' HOSPITAL AND COLLEGE

ALTON 1937

1. Alton Park Station — Private Siding
2. Laundry
3. Power House
4. Pharmacy
5. Isolation Hospital
6. College Recreation Hall, Dormitories, Dining Room etc.
7. College Workshops
8. Engineer's Quarters
9. Entrance
10. Museum
11. Garage
12. Hard Tennis Courts
13. Office Block
14. Florence Treloar Ward for Nurses
15. Kitchen and Dining Room Block
16. Silver Jubilee Treatment Centre
17. Observation Wards
18. Memorial Bust of Founder
19. Queen Alexandra Nurses' Home
20. Domestic Staff Quarters
21. Matron and Night Nurses' Quarters
22. Chapel
23. Assistant Resident Medical Officers' Quarters
24. Steward's Bungalow
25. New Quarters for Matron and Night Nurses
26. Trustees' Cottage
27. Medical Superintendent's Bungalow
28. Grass Tennis Courts
29. Portsmouth Block
30. Princess Royal Block
31. Connaught Block
32. Ward Block
33. Ward and Schoolroom Block containing Light Department, Splint Shop, etc.
34. Farm Cottage
35. College-Master's House
36. Tree planted by The Princess Alice
37. Tree planted by Lord Mayor Treloar

INDEX

The Author

Gladys Moynihan served with the S.O.E. (Special Operations Executive) in the Far East during World War II after which, as a member of the Foreign Office, she served in Germany, London and the British Embassy in The Hague and Vienna.

She married Mr. Francis Moynihan (Orthopaedic Surgeon) in 1955 and managed his private practice for the next 23 years. In 1959 they were actually living in "Jonah's" old bungalow. She is now retired but helps (on a part-time voluntary basis) at Lord Mayor Treloar College.

Alexandra House: Group photograph (by Kimroy Photographers) taken July 1988 on the occasion of the 40th anniversary of the takeover of the Hospital by the N.H.S.

Shown are: Mrs. Mary Andrews, David Bell, Mrs. Rita Bone, Ron Bowman, Miss Pam Bryant, Mrs. June Burt, Miss Susan Coates, Mrs. M. Craig, Mrs. Hilda Crawford, Mrs. Doreen Cuff, Ernest Farnham, Mrs. Audrey Ford, Mrs. Anna Graham, Mrs. Brenda Gregory, Sister Maureen Gunning, Mrs. Margaret Hampshire, Sister Valerie Henton, Mrs. Josephine Hounsom, Norman Hunt, Sister Frances Hutchins, Mrs. Barbara Ipsley, Terence McGilvray, Mrs. Anne Meacock, Miss Pamela Merritt, Mrs. C. Perkis, Sister Palmer, Sister M. Pitkia, Mrs. Patricia Quinn, Mrs. Pearl Russell, Sister Sally Smith, Mrs. Margaret Standing, Mrs. Gertrude Steen, Miss Geraldine Walker, Ernest Wilcox, Sister Ann Ward, Tony Wyeth.

159